Life Skills Literacy

Things to Know About Cars and Driving

by Richard S. Kimball
illustrated by Cecile Bayon

J. WESTON
WALCH
PUBLISHER
Portland, Maine

User's Guide
to
Walch Reproducible Books

As part of our general effort to provide educational materials which are as practical and economical as possible, we have designated this publication a "reproducible book." The designation means that purchase of the book includes purchase of the right to limited reproduction of all pages on which this symbol appears:

Here is the basic Walch policy: We grant to individual purchasers of this book the right to make sufficient copies of reproducible pages for use by all students of a single teacher. This permission is limited to a single teacher, and does not apply to entire schools or school systems, so institutions purchasing the book should pass the permission on to a single teacher. Copying of the book or its parts for resale is prohibited.

Any questions regarding this policy or requests to purchase further reproduction rights should be addressed to:

Permissions Editor
J. Weston Walch, Publisher
321 Valley Street • P. O. Box 658
Portland, Maine 04104-0658

1   2   3   4   5   6   7   8   9   10

ISBN 0-8251-3828-0

Contents

To the Teacher

Things to Know About Cars and Driving is another title in the growing *Life Skills Literacy* series from J. Weston Walch, Publisher. *Things to Know* books are reproducible and thematic compilations of information aimed at youth and adult English language learners, including ESL students new to American or Canadian culture. *Things to Know* books are intended to help build vocabulary, expand culturally-based knowledge, and develop real-life and survival skills. *Things to Know* books include interactive, authentic, cooperative, and idiomatic materials and activities. *Things to Know* books lead to success in the language and success in the classroom, the family, and the community.

The *Life Skills Literacy* series is appropriate for ESL learners at intermediate levels and for native learners reading at the fourth grade level and higher. Its vocabulary lists include more than 330 words and phrases, most of them specifically related to cars. Illustrative and contextual clues offer assistance with lexical development. Verb forms are generally simple, and the use of passive voice is limited.

The pages of *Things to Know About Cars and Driving* and its companion books can help individual students build reading and writing proficiencies. They can help full classes and small groups of students develop speaking and listening competencies as well. They can help all learners understand cars and driving, and explore related subjects like public transportation.

Their brevity and focus make *Things to Know* titles excellent resources for tutors working with individual students, whether the books are also used in the classroom or not. Their basic level makes *Things to Know* suitable to a wide range of circumstances and student abilities. Their controlled language and high-interest topics give *Things to Know* appeal for students as well as teachers.

Like other *Things to Know* books, this one devotes three pages to each of 24 lessons. The first of the three is for teachers. It provides information and suggestions ranging from general concept considerations to specific Internet sites you and your students might visit. The second and third pages are reproducible, for student use. The second presents topic information and a dialogue, story, or student challenge relating to it. The third includes a word list plus writing and discussion activities for individual, small group, and full class use.

This book cannot cover all automotive vocabulary or all car topics of possible concern to students. Nor can it be designed to be exactly at the level of each and every student. But it can be and is very flexible, covering the basics at a consistently low reading level and then offering numerous ideas for moving beyond and providing extension activities to meet a wide range of classroom and personal needs. General ideas for materials use and adaptation appear on the following page of Teaching Suggestions. More specific suggestions can be found on the teacher page provided with each lesson.

We believe you will find the Walch *Life Skills Literacy* series and its individual *Things to Know* titles useful with many different students in many different settings. We'll be pleased to hear how well it works for you, to know what other titles you think should be added to it, and—as always—to learn what more this company can do to serve you and your students.

—*J. Weston Walch, Publisher*

Teaching Suggestions

You can use *Things to Know About Cars and Driving* basically as is, having learners work through the two reproducible pages of each topic in one or two class sessions. Or you can make *Things to Know* the core of a broader approach to cars and driving by following the many suggestions in the topical Teacher Pages and expanding each lesson to cover several sessions.

The first step in deciding how to use these pages is, of course, assessing the needs, interests, and abilities of your learners. The second step is considering the characteristics of your own community. Wherever you teach, you'll find that your classes benefit most when knowledge of local laws and transportation systems is added to the *Things to Know* mix.

The "Preparation possibilities" of the Teacher Pages provide some ideas of what you might wish to do in advance to enrich your classes, particularly if you are presenting a lesson over several class sessions. But these pages are designed for immediate use, and you need not spend hours preparing for their presentation. If you think local information will be helpful to your groups, follow the suggestions of the teaching pages and assign students to do the research. They will become true learners and enjoy themselves as well when they discover the practical value of outside projects. Or invite outsiders to join the class and talk about such complex matters as insurance.

Some of the "Technology resources" suggested on the Teacher Pages assume an Internet connection and use of a search engine like Yahoo to look for information and suggested Web pages.

Each word list contains between 12 and 15 terms. Those about cars avoid the highly technical and should interest all consumers and drivers. The more general terms are all important to the passages in which they occur, and have been selected with reference to readability levels and vocabulary frequency-use studies. In some cases, you may want to adjust the lists to help meet the needs and interests of your own students. You can underline the words you wish to stress, tape over those you don't want, and add others you find useful. But be careful not to eliminate terms required for the fill-in sentences that follow.

The idioms and slang and the "fascinating facts" given in the teacher pages are presented as fun and informative extras for some classes. If you use the idioms and slang, consider asking students to try them in sentences and to share other terms they know. You can treat the word lists in the same way, if you like, asking students to build sentences around them and to supply related vocabulary that interests them.

All materials on the Activity Pages have been prepared with references to varied thinking skills, learning styles, and the several intelligences proposed by Howard Gardner and others. But no mix can be perfect for every class, and these also can and should be adjusted to meet the needs of your own groups. The role-plays based on dialogues, stories, and challenges are useful examples. Some students with very limited language skills will benefit from working in pairs and reading dialogues aloud to each other. More advanced students will enjoy and benefit from more creative approaches in which they make up their own parts and decide what might happen next to the characters in the story.

v

Lesson 1: Who Should Have a Car?

Themes:

- Assessing personal automotive needs
- Differentiating between *need* and *want*

Background notes: Assessing one's automotive needs can be complicated. The pleasures of the road and the siren call of advertising can lure even sophisticated consumers into purchasing cars they don't need and can't afford. Temptation and risk both rise dramatically for the young and inexperienced, especially those whose limited language skills make them vulnerable to the hard sell of the automobile market. So the following pages provide material you can use to help your students consider automotive needs and understand the differences between *want* and *need*. The words may sound simple. But understanding their relative importance can be tough. It requires knowledge of community geography and public transportation systems as well as personal and family circumstances and goals.

Preparation possibilities:

- Think about: alternative modes of transportation in your community
- Bring to class: information about local transportation systems

Technology resources:

- Search topics: *cars, automotive news, teenage drivers*
- Web pages to try: Automotive Industry News, Car Talk (public radio program)

Student pages:

- Page 2 includes: an introduction to *want* and *need;* a dialogue in which a teenager asks a parent for a car

- Page 3 includes: a word list you may adjust for your class and student activities

Especially for ESL: Counter any assumption that everybody in the United States and Canada has a car. Explain the difference between *need* and *want*: a *need* is something a person should or must have; a *want* is something it would be nice to have.

Extra idioms and slang to introduce:

- *New car bug*: strong desire to get a new car
- *Hard sell:* strong attempt to sell something

Thoughts to share with learners: Not everybody needs a car. Public transportation is better than private cars for some people in some areas.

Questions to ask learners: Who in the class has a car? Who uses public transportation? Why do you or don't you? Is it convenient? What does it cost? How can we decide what we *need* and what we *want?*

Projects to assign learners: Find out about local public transportation systems. Bring rate and schedule information to share with classmates. Report on your experiences with local transportation. Talk to friends and family members about cars. Do they have them? Are they pleased with them?

A fascinating fact to share: People in the United States spent $259 billion on cars in 1995. Some people want more public transportation. But car sales keep going up.

Name_____ Date_____

Lesson 1: Who Should Have a Car?

Many people love cars. The United States and Canada have **millions** of them. It may seem as if everybody has one. But that's not true. Some people walk to work and school. Some people take **public** buses. Some ride on a **subway**, and others use **bicycles**. Not everybody wants a car or needs a car, and not everybody has a car. What about you? What do you use for **transportation**? Do you want a car? Need one?

Dialogue: A Teenager Wants a Car

Teenager: I want a car. Can I get one?

Parent: You don't need a car.

T: I need a car so I can get a job.

P: You don't need a job, either.

T: If I get a job I can help the family. I can also save money for college.

P: But cars cost a lot.

T: I can get one for $500.

P: You can't get a good car for $500. A **cheap** car will need a lot of **expensive repairs**. You will also need to pay for a **driver's license**, **insurance**, and **license plates**.

T: I'll be a good driver. I won't have an **accident**, so I won't need insurance.

P: Accidents can happen to anybody. And the law in this state says that all drivers must have insurance. You will also need money for gas and **parking**.

T: That's why I need a good job. So I can pay those costs and still save money.

P: I didn't have a car when I was your age.

T: I know. But you had a job. You also walked to school and work. I can't even bicycle. School is so far I have to take a bus.

P: I did have a job. But I didn't save much money. Will you?

T: Yes. And if I say I will, you know I will.

P: Of course. I always trust you to do what you promise.

T: Then can I get a car?

P: But you can't even drive. You don't have a license.

T: I'll get **driver's training**. I can pay for that myself. Then can I get a car?

P: We can't **afford** a car for you.

T: We can if I get a job. What do you think?

P: I think we should talk tonight. Now it's time for school.

Life Skills Literacy:
Things to Know About Cars and Driving

Lesson 1: Who Should Have a Car?

ACTIVITY PAGE

Word List

million(s)	bicycle(s)	expensive	insurance	parking
public	transportation	repair(s)	license plate(s)	driver's training
subway	cheap	driver's license	accident	afford

Increasing Your Understanding

1. Look at the word list. If you don't know a word, find out what it means. Try to figure it out from the way it is used on page 2. Or look it up in a dictionary.

2. Supply the missing words from the word list:

    (a) The paragraph at the top of page 2 asks what you use for _____.

    (b) The parent in the story says a _____ car will need lots of expensive repairs.

    (c) "You will also need money for gas and _____," the parent tells the teen.

    (d) "I won't have an accident," says the teen, "so I won't need _____."

    (e) The teen has enough money to get _____.

Questions to Discuss

1. Does the teen in the story have good reasons to get a car? Does the parent have good reasons to say no?

2. What can you do if you need a car and can't afford one?

3. If you could have any car you want, what would it be like?

Things to Write About

1. Some people want big TV's, but most people don't need them. Write about something you want but don't really need. Explain why you want it.

2. Do you think it's a good idea to buy a cheap car? Why or why not?

Things to Do

1. Act out the story on page 2 with a partner. Use your own words if you want. Decide what you think might happen next. Write down some of your ideas.

2. Make a list of five reasons why some people need cars. Make another list of five reasons why some people do not need cars.

3. Draw a picture for the story on page 2.

4. What would your town or city be like if it had twice as many cars? Half as many? Would things be better or worse? Look around and decide. Then see if your classmates agree.

Life Skills Literacy:
Things to Know About Cars and Driving

Lesson 2: Who Can Drive a Car?

Theme:

- Licensing procedures

Background notes: Many young adults as well as newcomers to the United States and Canada learn about the process of acquiring a driver's license from friends and family members. But acquiring the language skills necessary to pass written and street tests may be a challenge. You can use the following two pages to help learners get started and understand what more they must do to become certified drivers. American states and Canadian provinces all have their own rules for and approaches to licensing drivers. Be sure that you understand the basics of those affecting your own students before introducing this topic. If you know of any students for whom early licensing is a critical need, be ready to spend extra time on this topic.

Preparation possibilities:

- Think about: the location of testing agencies and information sources
- Bring to class: a state or provincial driver training manual
- Invite to class: a representative of a local testing agency or driver training school

Technology resources:

- Search topics: *(your state) government* to *(appropriate agency)*

Student pages:

- Page 5 includes: a simplified portion of a typical license application for learner use, information about licensing, and a story about a test gone wrong

- Page 6 includes: a word list you may adjust for your class and student activities

Especially for ESL: Some licensing offices may offer help in the form of translators or printed materials in languages other than English. A phone call can determine their local availability. Ask: How do people get licenses in your native country?

Extra idioms and slang to introduce:

- *Ace a test*: make a perfect or almost perfect score
- *Blow a test*: fail it

Thoughts to share with learners: Applications and written tests can be tough. You can get help in driver training courses. In most places you can get sample test questions ahead of time. Another term for driver is "motor vehicle operator."

Questions to ask learners: How do you get a license locally? Where do you go? Who in the class has taken a test? How did you do? Do you know any funny stories about people taking driving tests?

Projects to assign learners: Go to the local motor vehicle office to get booklets and application forms. Fill out one of the forms for teacher or peer review. Interview friends and relatives who have taken the test.

A fascinating fact to share: America's first traffic law was passed by New York City in 1903.

Lesson 2: Who Can Drive a Car?

STATE OF _____						
APPLICATION FOR							
DRIVER'S LICENSE **EXAMINATION**							

PRINT NAME HERE	LAST NAME	FIRST NAME	MIDDLE NAME	MAILING ADDRESS		
LEGAL RESIDENCE						ZIP CODE
HEIGHT	WEIGHT	SEX	COLOR OF EYES	COLOR OF HAIR	DATE OF BIRTH	TEL NO.
Ft. In.	LBS	M or F			MO DAY YR	

You need a driver's license to drive. You may have to take two tests to get it. One is a **written test**, which asks questions about the laws in your state or province. If you know the law you pass the test. Then you take a **driving test**. That's when you show you know how to drive. You drive where a **police officer** tells you to go. You may also have to park. You need to do everything safely, and if you make too many mistakes, you may have to take the test again.

- -

Story: Ed Smith Has a Problem

Kim talked to her friend Ali on the phone.

"Did you hear about Ed?" she said. "He's in jail."

Ali was surprised. "Ed Smith? But I saw him two days ago. I talked to him about his driver's test. He was worried about it. He was afraid he would fail, and he needed his license for his job."

"Ed took his test yesterday," Kim said. "That's when he got in trouble."

"What happened? Did he hit a **pedestrian** or something?"

"No, he didn't have an accident," Kim said. "He drove very well, I understand."

"What went wrong?" Ali asked.

"Ed arrived for the test right **on schedule**," Kim told him. "Then he took the written test and answered every question right. I guess he knew everything he had to know about the law."

"That's great. So then what?"

"Ed took the driving part of the test," said Kim. "He drove with a police officer who told him where to go. They did everything, like making turns and **parallel** parking and stopping on a hill."

"So did Ed fail to stop at an **intersection**? Forget to **signal a turn**? Nobody gets **arrested** for that."

"Nope."

"Did he speed on Main Street? That's easy to do. I had a friend who did that in his test."

"No. They got off Main Street. This time the officer said to go to Eastern Avenue."

"Where the **police station** is?"

Kim laughed. "Yes. And when they got to the police station, the officer told Ed to stop. Then she arrested him. Now he's in jail."

"What in the world did she arrest him for?"

"Driving a stolen **vehicle**. The car Ed was driving belonged to the officer's mother. Ed stole it the night before the test."

"What a story!" said Ali. "And what a stupid thing to do!"

"You're not kidding" said Kim. "Now I've got to run. Bye."

"Bye."

Life Skills Literacy:
Things to Know About Cars and Driving

Lesson 2: Who Can Drive a Car?

Word List

application	mailing address	police officer	parallel	arrest(ed)
examination	written test	pedestrian	intersection	police station
legal residence	driving test	on schedule	signal a turn	vehicle

Increasing Your Understanding

1. Look at the word list. If you don't know a word, find out what it means. Try to figure it out from the way it is used on page 5. Or look it up in a dictionary.

2. Supply the missing words from the word list:

   (a) The form on page 5 is an _____ for a driver's license examination.

   (b) In the story, Kim asked if Ed hit a _____.

   (c) Ed was arrested for driving a stolen _____.

   (d) One thing Ed had to do was _____ parking.

   (e) On Eastern Avenue, the police officer said to stop at the _____.

Questions to Discuss

1. Why did Ed steal the car? What should he have done?

2. Why do you need to take a test to get a driver's license? Why not just drive?

3. How does it feel to take a test like a driver's test? What can you do if you feel nervous about taking tests?

Things to Write About

1. Fill out the application on page 5.

2. What was the hardest test you ever took? What was it for? How did you do?

Things to Do

1. With a partner, play the parts of Kim and Ali from the story on page 5. Use your own names if you want. Talk about what will probably happen to Ed.

2. Make a list of at least five things drivers should know.

3. What if somebody wrote a song about Ed? What would it say? Try writing it yourself. Get some help from a friend. Sing the song, too, if you want to.

4. What kind of tests do truck drivers and bus drivers need to take? Ask somebody outside your class. Then see if your classmates found the same information.

Life Skills Literacy:
Things to Know About Cars and Driving

Lesson 3: Kinds of Cars

Themes:

- Making choices in buying cars
- Coping with high-pressure sales tactics

Background notes:
Many students enjoy discussing the cars they would like to have. And many, especially the young, benefit from discussing how to decide on the kind of car to purchase. The following two pages on Kinds of Cars should help in the classroom and in real life—at the car dealership. Many things influence the choices that individuals make about buying cars. Some, like family size, are personal. Some are geographic; the convertible found frequently in California may be less popular in Minnesota. And some, like peer pressure and high-pressure ads, are questionable. You might usefully plan to spend some time helping students, especially young ones, consider the wisdom of choosing cars according to what their friends like.

Preparation possibilities:

- Think about: car dealers in your area—do some have better reputations than others?
- Bring to class: a recent newspaper showing a variety of cars and car sources

Technology resources:

- Page 8 includes: an introduction to the kinds of cars and choosing among them: a challenge activity about shopping for a car
- Search topics: *(your city or area) automobile dealers*
- Web pages to try: Ford, Chrysler, General Motors, Mitsubishi, Volkswagen, and others

Student pages:

- Page 9 includes: a vocabulary list you may adjust for your class and student activities

Especially for ESL:
Ask: Are the car makes and models you find here different from those in your native country? Did you or your family have a car there? What was it like?

Extra idioms and slang to introduce:

- *Cool:* excellent, neat
- *Snow job:* strong, misleading persuasion

Thoughts to share with learners:
If you are buying a car, remember that it's your money. You can listen to other people's advice if you want, but you don't have to. In 1998, the number of car dealerships was decreasing. One reason was the Internet. More people were using personal computers to buy cars.

Questions to ask learners:
If you have an old car and want a new one, should you trade the old one in at a dealer or sell it yourself? Is it better to buy a used car from a dealer or from an individual owner? What are the best places to get cars in your area?

Projects to assign learners:
Interview friends and relatives about why they chose their cars. Ask if they are pleased with them. Contact an insurance company to find out which types of cars are safest. Find out about how to register a car and report to the class.

A fascinating fact to share:
In 1997, the Toyota Camry became the best-selling new car in America. Toyota sold 397,156 Camrys that year. Ford Taurus had been the leader for the previous five years.

Lesson 3: Kinds of Cars

There are many different kinds of cars. How can you decide on one? Here are some choices you have to make:

new or used

domestic or **foreign**

expensive or cheap

the **make**—like Ford or Honda

the **model**—like Escort or Civic

the **style**—like van or four-door sedan

Reader Challenge: "I Want That One."

Salesperson: Looking for a new car?

Customer: Yes. I want to **trade** my old one **in**. It's that blue one over there.

SP: That looks like a good one. We'll pay you **top dollar** for that. Put you into something nicer, too. What style are you looking for? A **convertible**? A **sedan**? A van? A **station wagon**? A small truck? A two-door car? A four-door car? A sports car? What do you think?

C: Something **practical**. A four-door sedan, maybe.

SP: You sure? You'd look really good in that brand-new red convertible over there.

C: That's a beauty. But I've got a big family. And I can't afford a new car. I'm thinking used, maybe three or four years old.

SP: Okay. But buy a used car and you buy somebody else's problems. New cars might cost more, but they last longer.

C: Well, maybe. But show me some used cars first.

SP: What about makes? We have foreign makes and American makes. We've got

Fords and Hondas and Toyotas and Chryslers and everything else. So what do you think?

C: Too many choices. I think I'm getting confused.

SP: The best way to find a car is to drive some. Do you want to try the red convertible? Just to get the feel of a brand-new car? So you can **compare** it with the used ones? Besides, it's bigger than it looks.

C: No. I want to see some late-model used sedans.

SP: Okay, okay. But look at that green one over there. That's a beauty. It isn't used, but it's a **demonstrator** and we can give you a heck of a price.

C: _____

Here's your challenge: What would you say next if you were the customer? What should customers do when salespeople use **high pressure**?

Lesson 3: Kinds of Cars

Word List

ACTIVITY PAGE

domestic	style	sedan	demonstrator
foreign	trade (something) in	station wagon	high pressure
make	top dollar	practical	
model	convertible	compare	

Increasing Your Understanding

1. Look at the word list. If you don't know a word, find out what it means. Try to figure it out from the way it is used on page 8. Or look it up in a dictionary.

2. Supply the missing words from the word list:

   (a) The customer in the story wants to _____ an old blue car.

   (b) The salesperson uses _____ to try and sell a new car.

   (c) The customer wants something _____, like a four-door sedan.

   (d) The salesperson said the green car was a _____.

   (e) The list on page 8 says car buyers need to choose the _____—like Ford or Honda.

Questions to Discuss

1. How did you answer the challenge on page 8? Have you ever had trouble with a high-pressure salesperson? What did you do?

2. What is the most practical car style for you? For most people?

3. What's a good place to buy cars in your area?

Things to Write About

1. Would you like to sell cars? Why or why not?

2. How do new cars and used cars compare? Which is it better to get? Why?

Things to Do

1. Act out the story on page 8 with a partner. Decide how it ends, and act that out, too.

2. What if you bought a car today? What would your choices be? Use the list on page 8 and write down what you would choose for each item on the list.

3. Make a poster ad for a place that sells used cars. Give the place any name you like. Make it sound like the very best place to buy cars. Use pictures if you want.

4. Read the ads for used cars in a newspaper. Choose a car you want and tell classmates why you like it.

Lesson 4: Under the Hood

Themes:

- Learning about car engines
- Finding ways to get more information

Background notes: Computers, new power devices, and pollution controls have all helped in recent years to make car components more mysterious than ever to many owners. This fact places some owners at risk when dealing with maintenance and mechanics, a problem compounded when old vehicles and limited language skills are involved. Anything you can do to help your students learn more about cars should be helpful. Even some very basic information can be useful in communicating with dealers and mechanics. You may find during the discussions prompted by the next pages that some of your students have mechanical knowledge they will be happy to share. And you can help your classes identify other sources of assistance, from car manuals to school courses.

Preparation possibilities:

- Think about: local school courses and other sources of information
- Bring to class: your own car manual; copies of local newspaper columns about cars

Technology resources:

- Search topics: *automotive technician, automotive technician training*
- Web pages to try: The Car Guy (consumer information); Automotive Learning On-Line
- Software to consider: *Cars: The Essential Guide for Buyers and Owners*, CD-ROM published by *Consumer Reports*

Student pages:

- Page 11 includes: an introduction to automobile maintenance and a dialogue

between a parent and child about what is under the hood of a car
- Page 12 includes: a vocabulary list you may adjust for your class and student activities

Especially for ESL: Ask: How much car maintenance and repair do most car owners do in your countries? Are there dealers and mechanics in this area who communicate in your first language?

Extra idioms and slang to introduce:

- *Cool it*: relax
- *Wheels:* a car; also, *a set of wheels*

Thoughts to share with learners: Knowing even a little about car engines and maintenance can be very helpful. If you don't do the maintenance yourself, you should at least know what needs to be done when. "Automotive technicians" is another term used for car mechanics today.

Questions to ask learners: Who in the class understands car engines? How did you learn? What car makes have the best engines? Why do you think so?

Projects to assign learners: Bring car manuals to class and compare them. Which are easiest to understand? Find out about car courses offered at local schools. Find news stories about car engines.

A fascinating fact to share: There's a car in California that is 100 feet long. It has 26 wheels, a swimming pool, a king-size bed, and a helicopter landing pad. It is used mostly in films and for displays.

Lesson 4: Under the Hood

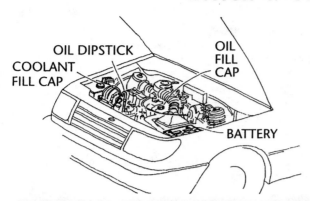

OIL DIPSTICK
COOLANT FILL CAP
OIL FILL CAP
BATTERY

Most people don't fix their own cars. They take their cars to **mechanics** for repairs. But they should know some things about their **engines**. They should know where to add **oil** and **coolant**. They should know where parts like the **battery** are. How can they learn these things? They can read their car **manuals**. Or they can ask a friend or mechanic to tell them. And some schools have **automotive** repair courses.

Dialogue: "I Want to See!"

Child: What are you doing under that thing?

Parent: That thing is the **hood** of the car. I'm looking at the engine.

C: What does the engine do?

P: It makes the car go.

C: What do you see?

P: I see a lot. I see the battery. I see the place to add oil. That will make the engine run well. I see the **dipstick** to measure the oil, and the place where I can add coolant. It says "coolant" on the fill cap. Coolant keeps the engine from getting too hot. I see a whole bunch of **wires**, too.

C: What are all the wires for?

P: They are part of the **electrical system**.

C: My friend's father has a truck. It has a huge engine. Does this little car have a small engine?

P: The car is small, but the engine is pretty big. It has four **cylinders** to help make the car go. This is a 140-horsepower engine.

C: Horsepower? What does that mean?

P: It means this engine can do as much work as 140 horses can. It means this car can go very fast.

C: Can it go faster than a car with just one horsepower?

P: Yes, it can.

C: I don't understand.

P: What don't you understand?

C: I don't understand about horses. How can a lot of horses go faster than one horse?

P: That's not so easy to explain. They can't. But lots of power makes cars run fast.

C: Lift me up, please. I want to see.

P: What do you want to see?

C: I want to see the horses.

P: I'll lift you up. But you'll be disappointed.

Life Skills Literacy:
Things to Know About Cars and Driving

Lesson 4: Under the Hood

ACTIVITY PAGE

Word List

mechanic(s)	coolant	automotive	wire(s)
engine(s)	battery	hood	electrical system
oil	manual(s)	dipstick	cylinder(s)

Increasing Your Understanding

1. Look at the word list. If you don't know a word, find out what it means. Try to figure it out from the way it is used on page 11. Or look it up in a dictionary.

2. Supply the missing words from the word list:

   (a) The paragraph at the top of page 11 says most people take their cars to _____ for repairs.

   (b) One way people can find out about their cars is to read their car _____.

   (c) The parent in the story is looking under the _____.

   (d) One thing the parent sees under the hood is the _____ to measure oil.

   (e) Another thing under the hood is a whole bunch of _____.

Questions to Discuss

1. Do most people know enough about their cars? What does page 11 say? Do you agree?

2. What are three good reasons to fix your own car? What are three good reasons to take it to a mechanic?

3. What if you don't know much about car engines? Can you still buy a good used car? How?

Things to Write About

1. Some cars are big with lots of horsepower. Some are small, with less power. Which kind would you buy? Why? Give at least two reasons.

2. You are buying a car. The salesperson lifts up the hood. What should you ask about the engine? Write at least three questions.

Things to Do

1. Act out the story on page 11 with a partner. Try to act like a real parent and a real child. What will the child say after looking at the engine?

2. What if you need to know more about your car engine? Where can you get help? Write the names of three people or places you could go to.

3. What do car ads say about engines? Watch some TV ads for new cars, and write down five things they say about engines. Share your list with your class.

4. Read the ads for used cars in a newspaper. Choose a car you want and tell classmates why you like it.

Life Skills Literacy:
Things to Know About Cars and Driving

Lesson 5: Outside Cars

Themes:

- The concepts of performance, style, safety, convenience, durability
- Washing and waxing cars

Background notes: Car care varies remarkably from individual to individual and by geographic area. In some places, like Los Angeles, many people seem to devote much time to keeping their cars shiny. In others, car care is much more casual. This is one of several pages in this set that encourages careful car care. It may spark useful discussion among students who attempt to protect their automotive investments through frequent cleaning and those who generally ignore such tasks.

Preparation possibilities:

- Think about: local environmental challenges to cars, like road salt and air pollutants; local commercial and nonprofit car washes

Technology resources:

- Search topics: *car washes*; (for areas with limited water resources) *waterless car wash systems*

Student pages:

- Page 14 includes: an illustration showing important parts under a sedan; an introduction of *performance, style, safety, convenience, durability*
- Page 15 includes: a word list you may adjust for your class and student activities

Especially for ESL: Ask: How well do car owners care for their vehicles in other countries? How often do they typically wash them?

Extra idioms and slang to introduce:

- *Soup up*: add power to a car
- *Have a one-track mind*: think a lot about one thing, like Terry in the story

Thoughts to share with learners: Student clubs and other groups offer car washes to raise money in some areas. You can support them and get your car cleaned at the same time.

Questions to ask learners: How often do you wash and clean your own cars? Do you do the work yourself? What are the best soaps and waxes to use? Where can you get them? What are the best car washes in this area? What else can car owners do to make their cars last longer? How long can cars last? What can car owners do when there's a water shortage in an area? Which do most people care for more—the outsides of cars or the insides?

Projects to assign learners: Visit or call local car washes to find out their prices. Share this information with classmates. Copy the list of five things from the top of page 14 (*performance*, etc.). Ask friends and relatives which items are most important to them when they buy cars. Find somebody with an old car and ask them the secrets of keeping it going. Find out how old a car needs to be to get "antique" license plates in your area.

A fascinating fact to share: Anybody could buy a brand-new car for $125 in 1922. The Red Bug Buckboard car cost that much. It weighed just 245 pounds.

Lesson 5: Outside Cars

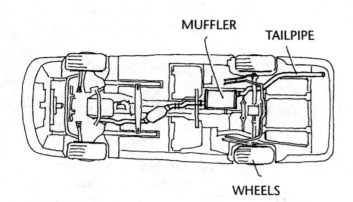

MUFFLER   TAILPIPE

WHEELS

Here are six things most people look for in cars:

Performance—How does it run?

Appearance—How does it look?

Safety—Does it have a good record?

Convenience—Does it have what you and your passengers need?

Durability—Will it last a long time?

Comfort—Does it feel good to ride in and drive?

Story: The Car Wash

Terry was washing his car when Sondra came by. "You do that all the time," she said. "You were washing and **waxing** your car just the other day."

"I spent a lot of money for this car," he told her. "I want to protect my **investment**."

"What about your body?" she said. "It's cold out here. And your arms must be tired from all that work."

"Don't worry," Terry said. "I'm working hard enough to stay warm. But I was cold when I used the **hose** under the car."

"I'm sure you were."

"But I needed to get the salt off the **muffler** and **tailpipe** and out of the **wheel housing**. That's where the **rust** can start."

"You don't want that," said Sondra. "You have a good, high-performance car here. You want it looking good."

"I love this car. It's safe. It's convenient. And it's got great style."

"Those all count a lot."

"Durability counts, too," he added. "If this car doesn't last, I'll need to buy another one

before I can afford it. And that may be never the way things are going right now."

"No money?"

"It's hard to save money when I'm **supporting** this car." Terry sighed. "Soap, oil, gas, insurance, license plates, all these things cost money."

"That's the price of driving in style."

"And that's another thing I worry about. Style. This car won't be in style when I want to sell it. So I'm losing money keeping it. But I would lose more money selling it. I can't win."

"Maybe not," she said. "But you have a beautiful car."

"Thanks. Want to go for a ride this afternoon?"

"Any place special in mind?"

"I'm going down to the **automated** car wash," he said.

"You're kidding!"

"No I'm not. You can't get a car too clean. And going through a car wash is cool."

"Okay," she agreed. "What time?"

Life Skills Literacy:
Things to Know About Cars and Driving

Name_____ Date _____

Lesson 5: Outside Cars

Word List

performance	convenience	wax(ing)	muffler	rust
appearance	durability	investment	tailpipe	support(ing)
safety	comfort	hose	wheel housing	automated

Increasing Your Understanding

1. Look at the word list. If you don't know a word, find out what it means. Try to figure it out from the way it is used on page 14. Or look it up in a dictionary.

2. Supply the missing words from the word list:

  (a) In the story, Terry invites Sondra to go with him to the _____ car wash.

  (b) Sondra saw him washing and _____ his car a few days earlier.

  (c) "It's hard to save money when I'm _____ this car," Terry says.

  (d) Terry wants his car to last. That's why he says that "_____ counts, too."

  (e) He washes under the car to get salt off the muffler and _____ and out of the wheel housing.

Questions to Discuss

1. Why does Terry wash his car so much? Do you think it's possible to wash a car too often?

2. Is Terry right about style? Is his car going out of style? Can he do anything about that? Why do car companies change the style of cars every year?

3. Which of the things at the top of page 14 is the most important if you are buying a car: performance, style, safety, convenience, durability, or comfort?

Things to Write About

1. Can you get people to take good care of their cars? Write a short newspaper article. Say why people should keep their cars clean.

2. What is a really old and rusty car like? Write a paragraph describing one. Tell how it got in such bad shape.

Things to Do

1. Act out the story on page 14 with a partner. Use your own words if you want. What if something funny happened at the car wash? What could it be?

2. How much can you save by washing your car? Do this math: You pay $30 a month to keep your car clean. How much is that a year? Your car lasts two extra years because it has no rust. You save $200 a month in car payments. How much is that a year? Subtract what you pay from what you save. How much do you save in two years?

3. Does your area have a lot of car washes? Make a list of those you could use if you wanted. What's the one closest to your school? Make a map showing where it is.

Life Skills Literacy:
Things to Know About Cars and Driving

Lesson 6: Inside Cars

Themes:

- The controls and gauges inside cars
- Using safety features and driving safely

Background notes: Safety is a necessary and important part of almost all course materials on cars and driving. It is presented here in conjunction with an introduction to driver controls. If most of your learners are already familiar with driver controls and the vocabulary describing them, you might wish to extend your discussion of safety. One topic that might provide good discussion is whether the government should require such safety procedures as fastening car seat belts and wearing motorcycle helmets.

Preparation possibilities:

- Think about: current news reports on automobile safety features like air bags and seat belts
- Bring to class: your car manual, especially if the controls are well illustrated

Technology resources:

- Search topics: *air bags, seat belts*
- Web pages to try: National Highway Traffic Safety Administration

Student:

- Page 17 includes: an illustration of some driver controls; a brief discussion of safe driving; a challenge activity asking students to name the most dangerous thing found in a car. Student opinions will vary. But the answer to which the instructor in the story seems to be heading when the student looks in the mirror is "the driver." Don't insist on this answer as correct, but do offer it if nobody else does.

- Page 18 includes: a word list you may adjust for your class and student activities

Especially for ESL: Ask: What are the words in your own languages for some of the controls and safety features discussed here? Are they similar to the English words? Do any driver training teachers in this area teach in your first language?

Extra idioms and slang to introduce:

- *Nut*: a crazy or eccentric person
- *Put the pedal to the metal*: push the accelerator to the floor

Thoughts to share with learners: An old saying goes like this: The biggest problem in the car is the loose nut behind the wheel.

Questions to ask learners: Do you always wear a seat belt? Should you? What does the law say? Can you think of a neat new safety feature for cars? Have you taken driver training? Where? Did the instructor help you prepare for both the written test and the driving test? Do you recommend the course?

Projects to assign learners: Read your own car manual and look at your own car. Make sure you understand all the safety features and controls. Call or visit some driver training schools. Ask how much they charge.

A fascinating fact to share: Nicolas Cugnot of Paris built the first automobile in the late eighteenth century. It was a steam-powered tricycle. Cugnot also had the world's first automobile accident. He crashed into a tree in 1769.

Lesson 6: Inside Cars

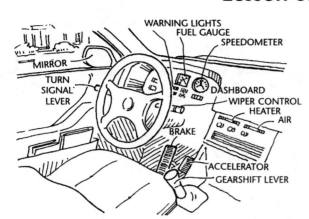

Cars can be fun, and many people need them. But we have to be careful with them. Thousands of people die every year in accidents. So we need to know as much as we can about cars. Drivers must understand how to drive. They also have to know the **safety features** of their cars. **Brakes** and air bags are important, but so is good driving. Only drivers can stop accidents.

Challenge: Danger in the Car

You are learning to drive. You are behind the **steering wheel**, and your teacher is in the other seat. She says to adjust your seat, and you do.

"I can see okay," you tell her. "And I can reach all the **pedals**. Now can I start up the car?"

"No," she says. "First, look around and tell me something. What's the most dangerous thing in the car?"

You know it's not the brake pedal. That makes the car stop, so it might be the safest thing. "Is it the **accelerator**?" you ask. "That makes the car go faster."

"No," she says. "The accelerator can sure cause problems, but it isn't what I'm thinking about."

"I know that air bags can be unsafe for children," you tell her. "But they aren't dangerous most of the time."

"That's right. Little children should ride in the rear seat so that the air bags can't hurt them. But the most dangerous thing in the car is something else."

You look at the **dashboard**. The **speedometer** can help you drive at safe speeds. The other **gauges** and **warning lights** give you information to help you drive safely. And seat belts are safe. That's what they're for.

"Are you sure this dangerous thing is inside the car and not outside?" you ask.

"Dangerous things are everywhere when you drive," she answers. "But the most dangerous thing is inside the car. So look around and tell me what else you see."

You tell her that you see the **air conditioning** and **heater controls**. You see the **turn signal** and the **gearshift lever** and the **wiper** control. And you see the **rearview mirror**.

"What do you see that's dangerous?" your teacher asks again.

Here's your challenge: What do you say? What do you see that's dangerous? What's the most dangerous thing in the car?

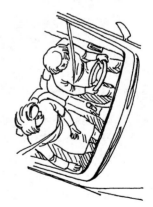

Life Skills Literacy:
Things to Know About Cars and Driving

Name_____ Date _____

Lesson 6: Inside Cars

Word List

safety feature(s)	pedal(s)	speedometer	air conditioning	gearshift lever
brake(s)	accelerator	gauge(s)	heater control(s)	wiper
steering wheel	dashboard	warning light(s)	turn signal	rearview mirror

Increasing Your Understanding

1. Look at the word list. If you don't know a word, find out what it means. Try to figure it out from the way it is used on page 17. Or look it up in a dictionary.

2. Supply the missing words from the word list:

   (a) When the story on page 17 opens, you are behind the _____.

   (b) The last thing you see in the story is the _____.

   (c) You tell your teacher that the _____ makes the car go faster.

   (d) When you look at the dashboard, you see the _____. It can help you drive at safe speeds.

   (e) The paragraph at the top of page 17 says people have to know the _____ of their cars.

Questions to Discuss

1. How did you answer the challenge? Is there more than one good answer?

2. Have you seen some dangerous drivers? What were they doing? Share your stories in class.

3. Can you think of a new law to make drivers safer? Brainstorm your ideas with class-mates.

Things to Write About

1. Who is the safest driver you know? Write a paragraph about that person. Why is he or she such a good driver?

2. What if a bee gets into a moving car? Write three things a driver should do or should not do.

Things to Do

1. Role-play the parts of a driving teacher and student with a partner. Talk about how to drive safely. Or talk about the controls in the car. What do they do?

2. The word list names some things you find in cars. What are some others? Make a list of at least seven things.

3. Can you make children safer? Make up a radio safety ad telling people to drive care-fully near schools and school buses. Tell it to your class the way you would say it on the radio.

4. Do you learn better by seeing real things? Then sit in a car and see if you understand all the controls. If you don't, ask somebody else. Or look in the car's manual.

Life Skills Literacy:
Things to Know About Cars and Driving

Lesson 7: Paying for Cars

Theme:

- Applying for car loans

Background notes: Getting a car loan is yet another promising but perilous step in the process of acquiring a vehicle. Even the knowledgeable may find seeking a loan tiresome and confusing. Be aware that unscrupulous lenders are eager to take advantage of consumers with little money, limited language skills, and a lot of lust for a new car. Watch for information about such people in your area, and be prepared to steer students away. And remember that the good guys are out there, too. Many banks and dealers offer good, ethical service. Government bodies at various levels have together passed myriad laws to protect consumers. There is great hope for the wary.

Preparation possibilities:

- Think about: how much information your students might want about car loans and banking; asking a banking representative to speak to your class; scheduling a field trip to a bank
- Bring to class: bank pamphlets about car loans; loan application forms

Technology resources:

- Search topics: *car loans, credit reports, debt counseling*

Student pages:

- Page 20 includes: a simplified list of things needed to get a car loan; an introduction to paying for cars; a dialogue about getting a car loan
- Page 21 includes: a word list you may adjust for your class and student activities

Especially for ESL: Moving to a new country can be frightening. Some newcomers have an understandable wish to stick close to their own neighborhoods and communities. You might wish to encourage some of your learners to search widely when seeking the best car loans. Minor differences in interest rates can make important personal differences.

Extra idioms and slang to introduce:

- *Loan shark*: somebody who lends at high interest rates
- *Deadbeat*: somebody who borrows money and doesn't pay it back

Thoughts to share with learners: Not all sources of car loans are equal. Be careful of lending companies that promise they will give instant credit and not refuse anybody. Their rates may be higher than those charged by banks and dealers. Interest rates are controlled by law. "Usury" refers to interest rates that are very high.

Questions to ask learners: Why do some people get turned down when they ask for loans? What can they do? Should people borrow money from friends and relatives for cars and other things? What could go wrong? How could you be sure everybody got a good deal?

Projects to assign learners: Call or visit local banks and car dealers and ask about their interest rates. Who charges the least for new car loans? Who charges the least for used car loans? Get and share a loan application from a bank.

A fascinating fact to share: In 1998 a Rolls Royce Silver Spur sedan was on sale for $189,900. How much would the payments be for something like that?

Lesson 7: Paying for Cars

It is good to save your money and pay cash when you buy a car. But many people can't do this. They need a job to get the cash, and they need a car to get a job. So they **borrow** money to get the car. Banks and **credit unions** and car dealers can **lend** you money for a car. Then they charge you **interest** for using their money. That can be expensive, so you need to know a lot about loans before you get one. This list shows a few things you might need to get a car loan from a bank.

Dialogue: Steps and More Steps

Banker: What can I do for you?

Customer: I just got a job. Now I need a car to get to the job, so I want to get a car loan. Can you tell me how to do that?

B: Yes. I'll tell you the steps you need to take to get a car loan. The first step is to find a car you want to buy and think you can afford.

C: That's pretty easy. The dealer down the road has a lot of cars I want. Some of the used ones are cheap.

B: After you find a car, the next step is to come in and fill out some forms. They will tell us about you and your **ability** to pay for the car. They will also tell us about the car you want and how much it will cost.

C: What's the step after that? Is that when the bank tells me how much it will lend me? Will you also tell me how much interest I will have to pay?

B: Yes. And in the step after that you need to decide if you want the loan. Before that, I recommend that you shop at a credit union and a car dealership for a loan. You need to decide the best deal for you.

C: Thank you for that advice. Is shopping for the best loan the last step?

B: No. We probably won't lend you all the money you need. So you need to find some money for a **down payment**. That's another whole step.

C: I almost forgot to ask. What about insurance?

B: That's still another step. You need to have insurance before you can borrow money from us.

C: Those are a lot of steps. I have a lot to do.

B: Yes, and you may need to take some steps twice.

C: Never mind. I am going to take some different steps.

B: What do you mean?

C: I will take the steps needed to walk to work until I save up enough cash for my car.

Lesson 7: Paying for Cars

Word List

loan	copy	child support	borrow	interest
proof	pay stub	rental	credit union(s)	ability
income	tax return	retirement	lend	down payment

Increasing Your Understanding

1. Look at the word list. If you don't know a word, find out what it means. Try to figure it out from the way it is used on page 20. Or look it up in a dictionary.

2. Supply the missing words from the word list:

   (a) The list at the top of page 20 tells what you need to get a _____.

   (b) The list includes a copy of a pay stub and a copy of a recent _____.

   (c) The paragraph says people who need cash for a car sometimes _____ money.

   (d) Borrowing money isn't free. Banks charge you _____ for using their money.

   (e) The banker in the story says the customer will need money for a _____.

Questions to Discuss

1. Why do you think the customer in the story decides to save for a car? Is that a good decision?

2. Look at the list at the top of page 20. Why do banks ask for information like that? Do they have a right to know such things?

3. Banks, dealers, credit unions, and other places give car loans. How can you decide which place is best for you? Brainstorm some of the steps you should take to decide.

Things to Write About

1. When is it better to save for something? When is it better to get a loan?

2. Say you have a car loan. But last month a member of your family was sick. You needed to help them, so you missed a car payment. But now the person is well, and you got a raise at work. You can pay the bank twice next month. Write a letter to the bank explaining this.

Things to Do

1. Act out the story on page 20 with a partner. Decide what you think might happen next. What will the banker say?

2. What are five ways to get money for a car? Make a list.

3. How can car dealers get customers to apply for their car loans? Make a sign about loans for a dealer's window.

4. Collect some newspaper ads for car loans. Which ones sound best? Number your three top choices.

Life Skills Literacy:
Things to Know About Cars and Driving

Lesson 8: Shopping for Cars

Themes:

- Finding a good buy in cars
- Using self-knowledge to avoid bad purchases

Background notes: If you have ever been personally bitten by the new/used car bug, you know the temptations your students face. Dealers use every attraction they can think of to lure customers into purchases. Even their own senses can work against customers' better instincts as they smell the new car smells and hear the satisfying "thunk" of tight doors closing. (See Activity 4 under "Things to Do" on page 24.) Among the things that can help car shoppers are product knowledge, familiarity with sales practices, and self-understanding. These pages touch on all those topics.

Preparation possibilities:

- Think about: the sales techniques you have experienced when shopping for cars; visiting a dealership with a small group of students

Technology resources:

- Search topics: *car dealers* (by geographic area)
- Web pages to try: Consumer's Checkbook, Edmund's (car prices, information)

Student pages:

- Page 23 includes: an illustration of a used car lot; thoughts about shopping for cars; and a story about shopping for cars and shoppers' self-understanding
- Page 24 includes: a word list you may adjust for your class and student activities

Especially for ESL: New learners may not understand that real negotiation is expected and accepted in many car dealerships. Ask: Could you bargain about prices in your first country for cars? Other items?

Extra idioms and slang to introduce:

- *Drive a hard bargain:* negotiate effectively and win a good deal
- *Sticker shock:* the dismay people feel when seeing the high prices on stickers in car windows

Thoughts to share with learners: It is sometimes best to shop for cars by visiting lots and looking at prices when dealerships are closed—on Sundays in many areas. That way you avoid sales pressure. It may seem that you must have that one special car you have found. But if the price isn't right, forget it. That feeling will go away, and there are a lot of cars for sale out there. Car buyers can sometimes save money by going where the bargains are, instead of insisting on only one popular make and model of car.

Questions to ask learners: How good are you at resisting sales pressure? Can you walk out of a dealership or store if a salesperson is pushing too hard? What can you do to get better?

Projects to assign learners: Visit a car dealership. Listen to salespeople and their customers. What do salespeople do to get customers interested? To close deals? How do you shop for cars without being pressured? What can you do to understand yourself better?

A fascinating fact to share: Car manufacturing was the fastest-growing industry in history, at least until the invention of computers.

Lesson 8: Shopping for Cars

To drive a car safely and well, you need good training and a lot of experience. To shop for a car and get a good buy, you need a lot of knowledge. You need to **investigate** cars, dealerships, and car loans. If you don't, you might buy a car that isn't very good. Or you might pay too much for the car you get. Or you might choose a car you can't afford.

Story: "I Need to Stop Shopping!"

On Saturday I asked my friend Alex if I could help him look for a car. "We'll do some quick **comparison shopping**," I said. "No **pressure** to buy. Just looking."

"Not me," he said. "I want to stop shopping for a car."

"But why? I know you want a car."

"Yes," he said, "but I can't afford one."

"But you can look and learn about cars now," I said. "Then you'll know what to get later."

"I do need to know more about cars," he answered. "But I already know a lot about me. My **negotiating** skills aren't so hot, and sometimes I can't say no."

"You mean you might get a car that costs too much."

"Right. If I find a **bargain** I might let some salesperson talk me right into a **contract**. Then there would be some sort of expensive **maintenance agreement**. Even if I didn't need it because the **warranty** would cover the car for at least six months. So I'm trying to stop shopping."

"Trying? You make it sound hard."

"It is," he answered. "I see cars for sale everywhere. They are in the newspaper's **classified** ads and the **display** ads. They are on television. They are at the dealerships when I ride by on the bus. They are on the roads with "for sale" signs on them. Some of them are great! So I'm staying away."

"I think you're wise," I told him. "A good salesperson might **convince** you to spend more than you should."

"That happened last year," he said. "I am still paying for some furniture I bought. So it's no car for now."

"That's a good lesson."

"It's an expensive lesson."

Life Skills Literacy:
Things to Know About Cars and Driving

Lesson 8: Shopping for Cars

Word List

make a deal	comparison shopping	bargain	warranty	convince
money down	pressure	contract	classified	
investigate	negotiating	maintenance agreement	display	

Increasing Your Understanding

1. Look at the word list. If you don't know a word, find out what it means. Try to figure it out from the way it is used on page 23. Or look it up in a dictionary.

2. Supply the missing words from the word list:

   (a) In the story on page 23, a friend asks Alex to do some quick _____.

   (b) After the contract, Alex said that there might be some sort of _____.

   (c) He wouldn't need the maintenance agreement if the car had a _____.

   (d) Alex says his _____ skills aren't so hot.

   (e) The paragraph at the top of the page says you need to _____ cars, dealerships and car loans before you buy a car.

Questions to Discuss

1. Do you think it was better for Alex not to shop for cars? Or was he being silly?

2. Do a lot of people buy things when they shouldn't? What can they do to avoid that?

3. How often do you see or hear car ads? Is it every day? Which ads do you think are best? Why? Can ads really convince you to buy things you should not get?

Things to Write About

1. How do you learn best? When you want to learn about things like cars, what do you do? Read? Listen to a friend? Look at cars? Write a paragraph saying how you like to learn things.

2. Did you ever buy anything you should not have? How did it happen? Tell the story.

Things to Do

1. Act out the story on page 23 with a partner. Use your own words if you want. Decide what you think might happen next if Alex went to a car dealer. Write down your ideas.

2. How would you sell cars if you were a dealer? Brainstorm with some classmates. Find things that appeal to senses like hearing and smelling. Decide at least three things to do.

3. Make a short radio play about a salesperson putting pressure on a customer. The customer likes a car but can't afford it. The salesperson says to buy it anyway.

4. Look at some car dealerships. Which look like the best places to shop? Why? If you can't go to the dealerships, look at their ads in a newspaper. Tell your classmates what you think.

Life Skills Literacy:
Things to Know About Cars and Driving

Lesson 9: Advice About Cars

Themes:

- Getting and assessing advice about cars
- Resources available through libraries

Background notes: Consumer advice about cars is plentiful. It's on the Internet and radio, in libraries, newspapers, magazines, and more. In fact, an Internet resource in 1997 listed 57 magazines devoted to cars. But not all advice is equal. Some is good, and some is suspect. You can't help your learners deal in advance with all the advice they will hear, of course. But you can help equip them to sort the helpful from the questionable. These pages introduce your learners to some good general sources like libraries, and good specific sources like *Consumer Reports* magazine. The pages also talk about how to judge advice, and suggest discussion of topics like dealing with a friend whose advice may not be very good.

Preparation possibilities:

- Think about: library resources available locally
- Bring to class: an automobile (April) issue of *Consumer Reports*

Technology resources:

- Search topics: *autos* to *buyers guides* to *media*
- Web pages to try: *Consumer Reports, Car Talk, AutoSite*

Student pages:

- Page 26 includes: some brief advice about getting advice, and a challenge story about one friend advising another to use library resources

- Page 27 includes: a word list you may adjust for your class and student activities

Especially for ESL: People from other countries may need extra help understanding the great diversity of available periodicals. Some are ad-driven and serve the auto industry while others do not. Ask: How are you used to finding car information in your first country?

Extra idioms and slang to introduce:

- *School of hard knocks*: experience
- *Know-it-all*: somebody who acts as if he or she knows everything

Thoughts to share with learners: *Consumer Reports* has no advertising. So it doesn't have to please any car manufacturer or other companies that are paying for ad space. That's one thing that makes it a very helpful magazine.

Questions to ask learners: Who in the class has used the Internet? Is it easy or hard? Is it useful? Did you do it through school or a library or somewhere else? Who in the class uses the public library? Is it helpful? Have you learned anything about cars "the hard way"? What?

Projects to assign learners: Go to the library or a bookstore and look for good books and magazines about cars. Try the Internet if you can. Do a class survey by having everybody ask a question like the one in Activity 4 under "Things to Do" on page 27.

A fascinating fact to share: In 1990, 84 percent of urban American trips were made in cars. Just 3 percent were made by public transportation.

Lesson 9: Advice About Cars

Advice is cheap and easy to get. But it can be tough to judge whether it's good advice or bad advice. If people don't know much about buying cars, their advice may not be helpful. Try to get advice from real **authorities**, who base their opinions on knowledge and experience. First decide what advice you need and where to get it. Then decide what kind of car you need and where to get it.

Challenge: Want Some Advice?

First Friend: I hear you're looking for a car. Want some advice?

Second Friend: No. Yes. I mean, I don't know.

FF: What's the matter?

SF: I already have too much advice. Everybody knows what I should do, but nobody agrees about just what that is. **According to** some, I should go to one dealer. According to others, that dealership is no good. If your car breaks down it won't **honor** its **guarantees**. I don't know who to listen to or where to go.

FF: I advise you to go to the public library.

SF: That's funny. The library doesn't sell cars.

FF: In a way it does. It has more stuff on cars than you can **imagine**. It has newspapers and magazines with ads. And it has computers with **Internet access**. That can lead you to **Web sites** selling new cars and used ones. And it can lead you to **consumer** advice about anything you buy.

SF: More advice. That's all I need.

FF: But this is good advice. Try *Consumer Reports* magazine. It's on the Web and

on paper at the library. It talks about **financing** cars so you know the best way to pay for them. If you want a used car, it has **frequency of repair** records. Those tell you how often each car breaks down. So you know which is most **reliable**.

SF: That sounds good.

FF: I'm heading to the library now. Want to go? We'll catch a bus together.

SF: Aren't you taking your car?

FF: I can't. My car is a **pile of junk**! It won't run!

SF: You have a terrible car? Then why should I take your advice?

FF: I'll tell you why. I learned the hard way not to listen to just my friends. Now I know enough to take my own advice and go to the library.

Here's your challenge: Will you go to the library? What's the best place for *you* to get advice?

Life Skills Literacy:
Things to Know About Cars and Driving

Lesson 9: Advice About Cars

Word List

advice	honor	Internet	consumer	reliable
authorities	guarantee(s)	access	financing	pile of junk
according to	imagine	Web site(s)	frequency of repair	

Increasing Your Understanding

1. Look at the word list. If you don't know a word, find out what it means. Try to figure it out from the way it is used on page 26. Or look it up in a dictionary.

2. Supply the missing words from the word list:

   (a) The second friend in the story on page 26 hears that one dealership won't honor its

   _____.

   (b) The first friend says the library has computers with _____ access.

   (c) The Internet can lead to Web sites and good _____ advice.

   (d) The paragraph at the top of the page says that _____ is cheap.

   (e) Only some of the people who give advice are real _____.

Questions to Discuss

1. How did you answer the challenge on page 26? Do you know somebody who is an authority about cars? Where would you go for car advice?

2. Imagine that a good friend is giving you advice about buying a car. But you don't think your friend knows very much. What can you say?

3. What if two magazines disagree about one car model? One says it is great. The other says it isn't. How can you decide which is right?

Things to Write About

1. Did you ever follow bad advice about a car? About something else? Tell the story.

2. Can you give advice about buying a used car? What if a friend asked you how to get started? Write a letter to that friend.

Things to Do

1. Act out the story on page 26 with a partner. Use your own words if you want. Imagine that the friends go to the library together. What do you think will happen there?

2. Make a list of five good ways to get advice about cars.

3. Make a poster for your local library. It should tell people to visit the library for information about cars.

4. Make up one question about cars. It might be something like this: "What is the safest car to drive?" Ask three people outside the class. Then report back to the class on what you learned.

Lesson 10: Maintaining Cars

Themes:

- The basics of maintenance
- Taking care of your own car

Background notes: Routine car maintenance is less burdensome than it used to be. Some auto manufacturers now claim that new cars can go 100,000 miles without a tune-up. That's because engines have changed so much. Electronic systems with no moving parts have replaced mechanical parts such as the often-temperamental carburetors. But even new cars are not maintenance-free. They still require such things as tire rotation, oil and filter changes, and replacement of belts according to manufacturers' recommendations. You can use these pages to help your students recognize this fact, to know how to care for their own vehicles, and to discuss good services in your area.

Preparation possibilities:

- Think about: maintenance services available in your area
- Bring to class: ads for low priced and competing maintenance services

Technology resources:

- Search topics: *auto maintenance*; specific services
- Web pages to try: The National Institute for Automotive Service Excellence and links

Student pages:

- Page 29 includes: some recommendations about maintenance and a dialogue about how and where to get maintenance done
- Page 30 includes: a word list you may adjust for your class and student activities

Especially for ESL: You might wish to mention the difference between the metric and U.S. systems of measurement. Many ESL students may be accustomed to metrics—measuring oil in liters, for example, rather than quarts. Ask: How did you get car maintenance done in your first country?

Extra idioms and slang to introduce:

- *Top off:* add a little liquid to something that is almost full
- *Spare tire:* a roll of fat around a person's waist

Thoughts to share with learners: It's easy for many of us to postpone such things as oil changes, especially when cash is short. But that can be costly in the long run. It's important to save records of all the maintenance services and repairs you get, to show buyers when you sell the car, or in case something goes wrong.

Questions to ask learners: Who in the class changes the oil in their own cars? Is it easy? Why do you do it? What does it mean to be "good with your hands"? Are you good with yours? How do people get that way? Where do you have your routine maintenance work done? What about repairs? Do you recommend these places? Do you pay an hourly labor charge? How much? Does that seem high? What does the money go for? Does the mechanic get it all?

Projects to assign learners: Research the cost of oil changes in your area. Ask the price of changing the oil and oil filter in a 1996 Ford Taurus. Who does the cheapest work? Share your information in class.

A fascinating fact to share: A brand-new car depreciates about 20 percent almost immediately after it is purchased.

Lesson 10: Maintaining Cars

Here are some maintenance **recommendations**. They will help you keep your car in good condition:

1. Drive carefully.

2. Do what your car manual says.

3. Learn about cars. Know what needs to be done.

4. Take your car to a good mechanic.

Dialogue: What Sam Does

Visitor: Hi, is Sam here? I've got something for him.

Occupant: Sam is out back. Look through this window. Those are his feet sticking out from under his car.

V: What's he doing?

O: He's **changing** the **oil** and the oil **filter**. Sam does all the maintenance work on his car.

V: That's what he told me. I guess he's taking a car repair course.

O: That's right. Last night he **rotated** the **tires**. This weekend he may do a whole **tune-up** and put in new **spark plugs**. He pays for parts, but he saves a lot in **labor charges**.

V: That sounds like a lot of work to me. But Sam said that finding other people to do the work is harder for him. He said that some mechanics are too busy, and some don't do good work. They have bad **reputations**.

O: It's hard to know where to take your car. Should you go to the **service department** at the dealer where you got it? To a mechanic at a garage? Or **specialty** places?

You know, a **repair shop** for the brakes and one for the muffler and one for tune-ups and one for tires?

V: I go to places like that. But I got new **drive belts** at my dealer last week. I'm no good at mechanics.

O: Sam is. He does everything he learns in school to his own car.

V: Has he studied tailpipes yet?

O: I think that's next week.

V: Good. Sam gave me a lift last night. And this morning I found part of his tailpipe in my **driveway**. That's what I want to give him.

O: I see Sam crawling out from under his car. So you can do that now. He'll be glad to have a job for next week.

Life Skills Literacy:
Things to Know About Cars and Driving

Name_____ Date _____

Lesson 10: Maintaining Cars

Word List

recommendation(s)	tune-up	service department	driveway
changing oil	spark plug(s)	specialty	
filter	labor charge(s)	repair shop	
rotate(d) tires	reputation(s)	drive belt(s)	

Increasing Your Understanding

1. Look at the word list. If you don't know a word, find out what it means. Try to figure it out from the way it is used on page 29. Or look it up in a dictionary.

2. Supply the missing words from the word list:

   (a) The list at the top of page 29 gives some maintenance _____.

   (b) The occupant of the house says Sam is changing the oil and the oil _____.

   (c) Part of Sam's tailpipe was found in the visitor's _____.

   (d) The visitor uses _____ places for things like tune-ups and brake repairs.

   (e) Sam knows of some poor mechanics with bad _____.

Questions to Discuss

1. Do you agree with the visitor that specialty places are good places to take a car? Are they better than the service departments of dealers? Why or why not?

2. What's the easiest way to learn about fixing cars? By doing it? By reading a book? By taking a course? Some other way? Do different things work best for different people?

3. How can cars become unsafe if they are not well maintained? What can happen then?

Things to Write About

1. Imagine that you take your car for an oil change. On the way home, you hear a strange noise. You look under the hood and find an empty oil container. Write what you will tell the mechanic.

2. Imagine that you can choose between two used cars. One costs $5,000. It comes with a record showing that the first owner did the maintenance just right. The other costs $4,000. It looks good, but it has no record. Will you take a chance and get the cheaper car? Write a paragraph saying what you will do and why.

Things to Do

1. Act out the story on page 29 with a partner. Use your own words if you want. Decide what you think Sam might do to his car next.

2. Make a list of five things people need to do to maintain their cars.

3. Make up a radio ad for a shop named Oliver's Oil Changes. Make it a song if you want to. Say it or sing it to the class the way you would give a real radio ad.

4. What kind of specialty-car shops are there in your area? Look around outside of class and make a list. Then share it with the class.

30

Life Skills Literacy:
Things to Know About Cars and Driving

Lesson 11: Checking Used Cars

Themes:

- Judging used cars
- Consumer protection laws

Background notes: Used cars can have high value and bring great satisfaction—if they are carefully chosen with the aid of experienced mechanics. The following pages will help familiarize students with testing procedures for used cars. They also provide a starting point for discussion of important consumer protection laws. One of these is the federal law requiring that dealers place a Buyer's Guide in the window of every used car to give information about warranties and problems. Others are state "lemon laws." These vary, but in general allow individuals to get refunds or replacements if they buy "lemons"—cars with many problems.

Preparation possibilities:

- Think about: consumer laws governing your state or province
- Invite to class: the representative of the state attorney general's office or a local consumer agency to talk about how used-car buyers are protected

Technology resources:

- Search topics: *lemon laws*; *consumer protection*
- Web pages to try: Internet Advocacy Center, Edmund's Consumer Information Services

Student pages:

- Page 32 includes: a checklist for judging used cars and a story about shopping for a used car
- Page 33 includes: a word list you may adjust for your class and student activities

Especially for ESL: New residents of the United States and Canada are sometimes subject to discrimination in the marketplace. Ask: Have you ever had a problem with a car dealer because you came from another country? What can be done about such problems? Have all learners brainstorm answers.

Extra idioms and slang to introduce:

- *Hang tough*: stick to a position, as in bargaining
- *Flat out*: at full speed

Thoughts to share with learners: It's your dollar, and you need to protect it by being careful when you shop for a used car or anything else. "Caveat emptor" is a term that comes from Latin and means "buyer beware." Today's consumer protection laws help protect you from problems. And some used car dealers are very good and honest. But you still need to be very careful before you make a purchase.

Questions to ask learners: Have you ever had a problem buying a used car? Do you want to share it? Do you think we have enough consumer protection laws? Can you suggest new ones?

Projects to assign learners: Look for consumer protection agencies near you. Look in the newspapers and phone book. Find out if local used car dealers allow test drives. If so, does a salesperson always go with the customer? How long do most dealers guarantee used cars? Visit some lots and look at the cars to find out.

A fascinating fact to share: In 1990, Ralph Nader's Center for Auto Safety said the average car in its lifetime would need $7,480 worth of repairs and maintenance.

Lesson 11: Checking Used Cars

When you buy a used car, you need to be careful. Go to the library and learn about how to check used cars. Make a list of things you should look for. Take a long test drive over some rough roads if you can. Look at the repair records for the car. Be sure to ask if the car has been in any accidents. Ask a mechanic you trust to check the car. If you go to a dealer, choose a dealer with a good reputation. Be sure the dealer offers a good guarantee.

Story: "I Like This One."

You go to the **"pre-owned"** part of a car dealer's lot. You find a red sedan you really like, so you open the door and sit in it. You look at the mileage and that seems fine. The car has a safety **inspection sticker**, and that's good. You try the horn and it works.

A salesperson hurries over and asks you not to blow the horn. You get out and **apologize**. You ask for a test drive.

"I'm sorry," she says, "but I can't sell you this car."

"Why not? Is this car a **lemon**? I know about lemons. Everything goes wrong with them."

"No," says the salesperson. She adds something else but a car goes by and you don't hear.

You **thump** a **fender** with your fist to see if it feels strong. "There's no rust at all," you say.

"That's right," says the salesperson. "But . . ." And another car goes by.

You push down on a corner of the car. It only bounces once, so you know the suspension is good. Maybe you should get it checked at a **diagnostic test center**.

But the car doesn't have a **Buyer's Guide** sticker. The law requires that to say if the car is warrantied and if it has problems. You ask about that.

"I'm trying to explain," the salesperson says. "But please stop touching the car. You're getting **fingerprints** all over it."

"How can I buy a car if I don't touch it?" you ask. You open the door and **slam** it shut. It sounds great.

"Please don't slam that door again!" she tells you.

"You seem nervous about this car," you tell her. "Why? What's wrong?"

"I'm nervous because the car isn't for sale. It belongs to another customer. Here he comes now, and he looks angry!"

Life Skills Literacy:
Things to Know About Cars and Driving

Lesson 11: Checking Used Cars

Word List

mileage	inspection	lemon	diagnostic text center	slam
suspension	sticker	thump	Buyer's Guide	
pre-owned	apologize	fender	fingerprint(s)	

Increasing Your Understanding

1. Look at the word list. If you don't know a word, find out what it means. Try to figure it out from the way it is used on page 32. Or look it up in a dictionary.

2. Supply the missing words from the word list:

   (a) When the story on page 32 begins, you are in the _____ part of a dealer's lot.

   (b) Near the end of the story you open the door and _____ it shut.

   (c) The salesperson complains that you are getting your _____ all over the car.

   (d) The salesperson says she won't sell the car. "Why not?" you ask. "Is this car a _____?"

   (e) Two items in the checklist on page 32 are the suspension and the _____.

Questions to Discuss

1. In the story, the salesperson tries to tell you something, but you don't hear. What do you think she is trying to say?

2. Why do some dealers call their cars "pre-owned" instead of "used"? Do you see fancy words like that when you shop in other places? What are some? Do they make any difference to you?

3. The used cars in most dealer lots have prices on them. Is that what the buyer really pays for the car? Explain your answer.

Things to Write About

1. How can you know if a used car was in an accident? Write a paragraph saying what you would look for.

2. Imagine that you are buying a used car. What kind of person would you want the previous owner to be? Write a description.

Things to Do

1. Act out the story on page 32 with a partner. Use your own words if you want. The salesperson can be a man or a woman. What do you think the car's owner will say?

2. What should used car dealers say on their cars in writing? Make a list of at least five things you want to know about every used car you might buy.

3. Look at the checklist at the top of page 32. Think of two more things you think you should check when you are looking at a used car. Share them with your classmates to see if they agree.

4. What words are best for selling cars? Look at some used car ads outside of class. Write down the words that make you want a car. Share them with your class to see if other people agree.

Life Skills Literacy:
Things to Know About Cars and Driving

Lesson 12: Liquids of Cars

Themes:

- The liquids of cars
- The problems of aging cars

Background notes: Gas. Coolant. Oil. Automatic transmission fluid. Brake fluid. Windshield washer fluid. The list is a long one. And everything on it comes in different brands and at different prices, if not in different grades. Most of us don't spend a lot of time on such matters. We do what our manuals and mechanics tell us. But it's good to ask some questions some of the time: How much oil and other liquids are our cars demanding? How much are we spending on gas? Can we find better, cheaper sources if we break our habits and go somewhere else? These pages will help your students address these questions and the related question of when a car becomes too old and expensive to keep.

Preparation possibilities:

- Think about: gas prices in your community
- Bring to class: any ads you run across for inexpensive oil or other auto fluids

Technology resources:

- Search topics: *gasoline, oil, alternate fuel vehicles*
- Web pages to try: U.S. Department of Energy

Student pages:

- Page 35 includes: an introduction to the liquids of cars; a challenge story about a thirsty monster of an older car
- Page 36 includes: a word list you may adjust for your class and student activities

Especially for ESL: Some students might need help understanding how quarts and gallons compare to the liters of the metric system. (A quart equals .946 liter.) Ask: What did gas cost in your first countries?

Extra idioms and slang to introduce:

- *Run out of gas:* lose energy (said of a person)
- *Gas up:* get gasoline

Thoughts to share with learners: Sometimes we spend more than we need to out of habit. We go to the same stores and gas stations we have always been to. Sometimes we should look around and see if we can do better elsewhere.

Questions to ask learners: Where do you get gas? Why are gas prices so different in different parts of this country? The world? Maybe this community? Have you seen a gas war (when businesses keep cutting gas prices to take business away from each other)? What can be done about the pollution caused by cars? Do you like the idea of electric cars?

Projects to assign learners: Do some comparison shopping. Find out the cost of windshield washer fluid at different places and report back to the class. Find out how to get rid of old oil in this area.

A fascinating fact to share: In 1839, Charles Goodyear discovered how to make rubber more useful by a process called vulcanizing. The first solid rubber tires for bicycles came in 1845. John Dunlop developed pneumatic (air-filled) tires in 1888. They were first used for bicycles, but soon after on cars.

Lesson 12: Liquids of Cars

Do you want to save money on your car? Shop carefully for **gasoline** and other **liquids**. Get **regular unleaded** gas if you can, and pump it yourself. But don't drive too far for cheap gas. Getting there will cost too much. Add your own windshield washer, and check other liquids yourself. If you go to a gas station for an oil change, ask the price. Then compare it to what **"quick lube centers"** charge.

Challenge: The Monster

"I've got a **monster**," Lena told Chen.

"What?" said Chen.

"I've got a monster," said Lena. "A big, thirsty monster."

"And just where is this monster of yours?"

"In the driveway. Take a look."

Chen looked. All he saw was Lena's car.

"Is that what you mean? Your car?"

"Yes," she said. "My car is a gas **guzzling** monster. I only get about 10 **miles per gallon**."

"I see some oil on the driveway, too."

"Right. But most of the oil goes up in smoke. My monster burns a **quart** of oil a week. There's a cloud of smoke behind my car. If my family sees smoke down the road, they know I'm coming home."

"I hope you get a good price in oil," he said.

"Yes. I buy it by the case at a **discount** store."

"At least that's good. And I hope you don't get **high-test** gas."

"Nope. The monster likes regular, low-**octane** gas just fine," Lena said. Then she sighed. "But that's not all my monster needs. Last month I had to get **automatic transmis-**sion fluid. The month before it leaked brake fluid. I needed to have the brakes fixed."

"At least your brakes are good. Your monster can't run away."

"That's a good thing, because I couldn't chase it. The driveway is too slippery. There's not just oil there. There's some coolant, too, where the **radiator** leaked."

"You do have a thirsty monster. But does the car run well?"

"Well, it's making a loud noise. My monster is beginning to roar. Maybe the muffler is getting loose."

"Better get it looked at."

"I know. But I am spending all my money on my monster. I'm broke. What should I do?"

Here's your challenge: Answer for Chen. What should Lena do? What's your advice?

35

Life Skills Literacy:
Things to Know About Cars and Driving

Name_____ Date _____

Lesson 12: Liquids of Cars

Word List

gasoline	unleaded	guzzling	discount	automatic
liquid(s)	quick lube center(s)	miles per gallon	high-test	transmission fluid
regular	monster	quart	octane	radiator

Increasing Your Understanding

1. Look at the word list. If you don't know a word, find out what it means. Try to figure it out from the way it is used on page 35. Or look it up in a dictionary.

2. Supply the missing words from the word list:

   (a) Lena says her car is a gas guzzler. She only gets about 10 _____.

   (b) There is coolant in the driveway because the _____ leaked.

   (c) Lena buys oil by the case at a _____ store.

   (d) The paragraph at the top of page 35 says to get _____ unleaded gas.

   (e) You should compare the price of a gas station oil change to what _____ charge.

Questions to Discuss

1. How did you answer the challenge on page 35? What should Lena do?

2. How long should people keep cars? How can you tell when it's time to get a different one?

3. Do gas guzzling cars hurt anybody but their owners? Who? Why? What about cars that burn a lot of oil?

Things to Write About

1. Is a discount store a good place to buy things for cars? Why or why not?

2. Describe a favorite car you once owned or rode in. It can be an old one, like Lena's, or a new one.

Things to Do

1. Act out the story on page 35 with a partner. Use your own words if you want. What else could be wrong with Lena's car? Write down your ideas.

2. Make up a story about a car that smokes a lot. One person in the class can start the story by making up one sentence. Then another person can make up the next sentence. Keep going like that around the room and see what happens.

3. Draw a picture showing what you think Lena's car looks like.

4. Is the price of gas the same everywhere you look? Check around your neighborhood and see. How many prices can you find? Talk with your classmates about what you find.

Life Skills Literacy:
Things to Know About Cars and Driving

Lesson 13: Fixing Damaged Cars

Themes:

- Having auto body work done
- Getting estimates

Background notes: American police received reports of 6,842,000 traffic accidents in 1996. Those accidents meant a lot of money to auto body shops—some of it well spent and some of it not. Getting a good bid for body repair work is difficult for several reasons: Most of us aren't familiar with local auto body shops because, fortunately, we don't use them very often. It is sometimes tricky to get a damaged vehicle to body shops for estimates. And most of us know little about auto body work or the language of its providers. But if you can help your learners understand procedures of obtaining and comparing competitive estimates, you can help prepare them for the challenge.

Preparation possibilities:

- Think about: what you have heard about local body shops
- Bring to class: ads or news stories about local body repair services

Technology resources:

- Search topics: *auto body repair*
- Web pages to try: National Highway and Traffic Safety Administration

Student pages:

- Page 38 includes: a simplified portion of a repair estimate form, an introduction to getting estimates, and a dialogue in which two friends discuss an accident one has had
- Page 39 includes: a word list you may adjust for your class and student activities

Especially for ESL: ESL students might need some extra help on the distinction between *major* and *minor*. Point out: The difference is sometimes specific ("major league" or "minor league"). But more often it's a matter of interpretation (the doctor's "minor operation" is "major" to the patient).

Extra idioms and slang to introduce:

- *Fender bender*: minor car accident
- *Totaled*: destroyed

Thoughts to share with learners: Almost everybody has trouble understanding some long and complicated printed forms—like the one mentioned in question 3 under "Questions to discuss" on page 39. If you have questions about a repair company, you can call your local Better Business Bureau and ask for a reliability report. The reports are also available on the Internet.

Questions to ask learners: Should you get estimates for all kinds of car repairs—not just body work? Has anybody in the class had car body work done? Where? Was it a good job?

Projects to assign learners: Visit a car body shop. Ask for a copy of a blank estimate form to share with classmates. Visit your local American Automobile Association and find out about membership. Ask what services the AAA offers, and decide if membership sounds like a good idea.

A fascinating fact to share: Americans now spend about $100 billion annually on auto repair. Consumer advocate Ralph Nader has estimated that $40 billion of that is unnecessary.

Body Repair Estimate

Body _____

Paint _____

Frame _____

Labor _____

Tax _____

TOTAL _____

I authorize the above work.

_____ _____
(signed)   (date)

Lesson 13: Fixing Damaged Cars

Here's part of a form for making **estimates**. When your car is **damaged**, shop around for a good price. Get estimates from several **body shops**. This will help you get repairs at a fair price. You also may need the forms for your insurance company. The lowest price you find may not be best. A cheap company that does bad work is no good. So find a good place and a good deal. Then **authorize** the work.

Dialogue: "I Need Some Body Work."

Steve: Do you know where I can get some body work done?

Jean: You should call your doctor. Or, if the problem is serious, you should go to the hospital.

S: You don't understand. It's not *my* body that needs the work. It's my car's body.

J: Then go to a body shop. I know a good one across town. It's called Collins **Collision** Center. They do wonderful work at low prices.

S: Maybe I'll take my car there for an estimate.

J: What happened? Did you have an accident?

S: Yes. Another car **skidded** on ice and ran into mine. It **smashed** my **headlight** and my front fender.

J: Was anybody hurt?

S: No. And I can still drive the car.

J: Is the **frame** okay?

S: I think so.

J: Good. The whole car rides on the frame. If it is bent you have big trouble. You were lucky.

S: I didn't feel lucky at the time.

J: I know. But you did not need an **ambulance** or a **tow truck**. You had a **minor** accident.

S: That's what the police officer called it. But it feels **major** to me. It will cost a lot, and I'm broke.

J: Do you have insurance?

S: Yes. But there's a big **deductible** I have to pay.

J: I still think you were lucky. And you can be lucky again if you take your car to Collins. They are very honest and they won't take advantage of you.

S: Okay. I'll be sure to try Collins. Hey, that's strange, isn't it?

J: What's strange?

S: The name. Your name is Collins, too.

J: Yes it is. Collins Collision Shop belongs to my brother. That's how I know it is good.

Life Skills Literacy:
Things to Know About Cars and Driving

Lesson 13: Fixing Damaged Cars

Word List

ACTIVITY
PAGE

| estimate(s) | body shop(s) | collision | smash(ed) | frame | tow truck | major |
| damage(d) | authorize | skid(ded) | headlight | ambulance | minor | deductible |

Increasing Your Understanding

1. Look at the word list. If you don't know a word, find out what it means. Try to figure it out from the way it is used on page 39. Or look it up in a dictionary.

2. Supply the missing words from the word list:

   (a) Steve's insurance has a big _____ that he has to pay.

   (b) Jean thinks Steve was lucky because he didn't need an _____ or a _____.

   (c) According to the police officer, Steve's accident was minor. But it feels _____ to Steve.

   (d) The paragraph at the top of page 39 says to get estimates from several _____.

   (e) You should find a good place and a good deal. Then _____ the work on your car.

Questions to Discuss

1. Should Steve go to Jean's brother? If he does, should he still get more estimates?

2. What if a body shop starts a job, then finds damage it didn't know about? Fixing it could cost more than the estimate said. Should the shop just do the work and charge the customer?

3. Imagine that a friend of yours has a damaged car. He gets five estimates to fix it, and finds a good body shop. It can do the work now, at a good price. He wants to authorize the work. But the form they want him to sign is very complicated. He doesn't understand it. What should he do?

Things to Write About

1. What should Steve tell his insurance company? The company sent him a form asking what happened. Write a paragraph for him describing the accident.

2. Why should your friend have car insurance? She writes you a letter and says she has a car. But she is driving without insurance. Write her a letter back. Tell her why she needs to get some.

Things to Do

1. Act out the story on page 39 with a partner. Use your own names if you want. Decide what might happen next. Will Steve go to Collins Collision Center? What will happen there?

2. What do you need to know from a body shop? If you take your car for repairs, you want to know the price. What else? List at least three things you need to know.

3. Make an advertising sign for Collins Collision Center. Use words and a picture of a car.

4. How can you find auto body shops? Try the yellow pages in your local phone book. Where are the body shops listed? How many can you find? See if your classmates find the same thing.

Life Skills Literacy:
Things to Know About Cars and Driving

Lesson 14: Car Parts

TEACHER PAGE

Themes:

- Replacing car parts
- Applying for a job selling car parts

Background notes: More than half a million outlets sell automotive products today. They include a surprising variety of retail establishments, from auto parts stores to convenience stores, from home centers to drugstores. In fact, together they represent almost a third of all retail establishments. And the business they do is enormous—an estimated $151 billion in 1997, according to the Automotive Parts and Accessories Association (APAA). These pages will help your students think about finding the best parts sources in your area.

Preparation possibilities:

- Think about: where car parts are sold in your area
- Bring to class: ads for local car parts suppliers; a parts catalog

Technology resources:

- Search topics: *car parts*
- Web pages to try: Automotive Parts and Accessories Association

Student pages:

- Page 41 includes: an introduction to car parts and a story describing an interview for a job working in a car parts store
- Page 42 includes: a word list you may adjust for your class and student activities

Especially for ESL: The car parts market may add an immense new vocabulary challenge for your learners. A good illustrated parts catalog could be very helpful to learners with an interest in this area.

Extra idioms and slang to introduce:

- *Tooting your own horn:* saying good things about yourself
- *Break down:* stop working

Thoughts to share with learners: You can get car parts through the Internet and by mail. You might find very good prices through catalogs and Web sites. But don't forget to think about shipping costs when you are comparing prices. They can be high, especially if you want something fast.

Questions to ask learners: Who in the class buys car parts? Where do you get them? Are you satisfied? What kind of information do you need to take when you get car parts? Is the model and year of your car usually enough? What kind of jobs are good for people who like cars? How many can you brainstorm?

Projects to assign learners: Choose a car part and do some comparison shopping. Maybe it will be a wiper blade for a 1996 Honda Civic. Compare what you find in class. What kind of places have the best prices? Dealers? Parts stores? Discount stores? Look in the paper for jobs working with cars. Do any sound good to you?

A fascinating fact to share: The 1997 sales of tires and inner tubes direct to consumers in the United States was estimated by the APAA at more than $18 billion.

Lesson 14: Car Parts

Cars have thousands of parts to wear out or break. A dealer can sell and **install** the **replacement** part you need. Or you can get it at a parts store and install it yourself. Sometimes you can buy used and **rebuilt** parts. Look for them at **junkyards**. They **salvage** them from **wrecks** and junked or **abandoned** cars. Good used parts can save you money. They take more work. But that's fun for some people.

Story: A Job in Car Parts

Ivan heard about an opening in a car parts store. He needed a job, so he applied to Rosa, the **manager**.

Rosa was looking for a person to help with sales. She asked about Ivan's **qualifications**.

"I have experience selling things," Ivan told her. "When I was in high school, I worked in a supermarket. I am good at working with people. I like cars, too."

"People who sell car parts must know a lot," Rosa said. "They need to know most about common car parts, like mufflers, oil filters, **wiper blades**, and batteries. They need to know about lots of less common car parts, too, like the pieces of **transmissions**."

"I already know a lot," Ivan said. "Last year I took my whole car apart."

"Did you get it back together all right?" Rosa asked.

"Of course," said Ivan. "Now I know the names and numbers of almost every part."

Rosa thought Ivan was a good **applicant** for the job. But she needed to know one more thing. "We sell thousands of parts," she said. "We have a huge **inventory**. Our **computer** helps

keep track of them. But we can't carry the computer with us. We need to remember what it says. How is your **memory**?"

"Great," said Ivan. "I have a really good memory. I can remember almost everything. That's my biggest strength."

"Good. Maybe I will hire you. Please put your name and phone number on this form. I'll call if I can use you."

"I'll leave my name," said Ivan. "But I need to call you later with my phone number."

"Why?"

"I can't remember it. It's new, and I forgot to write it down. That's funny, isn't it?"

He smiled at Rosa. But she didn't smile back.

"No," she said. "I'm afraid I don't think that is funny."

Name_____ Date _____

Lesson 14: Car Parts

Word List

ACTIVITY PAGE

install	junkyard(s)	abandon(ed)	wiper blade(s)	inventory
replacement	salvage	manager	transmission(s)	computer
rebuilt (rebuild)	wreck(s)	qualification(s)	applicant	memory

Increasing Your Understanding

1. Look at the word list. If you don't know a word, find out what it means. Try to figure it out from the way it is used on page 41. Or look it up in a dictionary.

2. Supply the missing words from the word list:

   (a) Early in the story on page 41, Rosa asked about Ivan's _____.

   (b) According to Rosa, the store had thousands of parts. "We have a huge _____," she said.

   (c) People who sell car parts need to remember things. So Rosa asked Ivan, "How is your _____?"

   (d) The paragraph at the top of page 41 says a dealer can sell and _____ replacement parts.

   (e) Junkyards _____ parts from wrecks and junked or abandoned cars.

Questions to Discuss

1. Did Ivan say the right things to Rosa? Should you overstate your abilities when you apply for a job?

2. When should you get new car parts? When should you get old ones? What do you think?

3. What if cars and car parts lasted forever? What would happen?

Things to Write About

1. Would you like to sell car parts? Imagine that you would. Write a letter applying for a job at World's Best Car Parts. Give at least three reasons why you would be good.

2. What if you invented car windows that didn't break? Write a paragraph saying what you would do.

Things to Do

1. Act out the story on page 41 with a partner. Use your own names if you want. What will happen next? Decide whether you think Rosa will hire Ivan.

2. What car parts last longest? Some things, like wiper blades, are replaced a lot. Other things, like seats, usually last as long as the car. List at least five more car parts that last a long time.

3. Can you sell car parts? Make up a TV ad for Sarah's Salvaged Car Parts with some other students. Act out the ad. The ad could have a salesperson and a happy customer in it.

4. What car parts wear out fastest where you live? (If you live in a rain forest, it may be the wiper blades.) What parts last longest where you live? Look around outside of class and decide. Then share your answers with your classmates. Do they agree?

© 1998 J. Weston Walch, Publisher

Life Skills Literacy:
Things to Know About Cars and Driving

Lesson 15: Car Options

TEACHER PAGE

Theme:

- The nature and value of car options

Background notes: Whole eras have passed since Henry Ford decreed early in the twentieth century that consumers could have a car in any color they wanted—as long as it was black. Even in those days, car owners could find a wide variety of aftermarket accessories to add to their cars after purchase (see the Fascinating Fact below). And today the options begin with car manufacturers. Customers can sit at their home computers if they want and design their own cars on the Web pages supported by manufacturers, watching total vehicle costs go up as they do. Used car buyers have fewer choices, of course, but the patient among them can often find the same features they would have requested in a new car. These pages will help your learners begin thinking about which options are important and which are not.

Preparation possibilities:

- Think about: which car options really help drivers and passengers?
- Bring to class: news articles or ads for options

Technology resources:

- Search topics: *car options*; manufacturers by name; specific options
- Web pages to try: Automotive Aftermarket World (trade journal)

Student pages:

- Page 44 includes: an illustration showing a few car options, an introduction to the general topic, and a challenge story about a car salesperson discussing options with a customer

- Page 45 includes: a word list you may adjust for your class and student activities

Especially for ESL: Having learners list the features in their own dream vehicles can help them build vocabularies. If your students lack the vocabularies necessary to generate such lists from scratch, consider listing some options for them on a chalkboard or handout.

Extra idioms and slang to introduce:

- *Stripped down:* a basic car with no added features
- *Fuzz buster:* radar detection device

Thoughts to share with learners: Some manufacturers offer options packages in their cars. These can lower the cost per option. But they may also force you to get some options you don't want in order to get some you do.

Questions to ask learners: What are your favorite car options? What would you get if you ordered a car today? What do you have on your own cars? Do you like these features? Will some of today's options become standard sometime (the way air conditioning is now standard in some new cars)?

Projects to assign learners: Find out about local public transportation systems. Bring rate and schedule information to share with classmates. Report on your experiences with local transportation. Talk to friends and family members about cars. Do they have them? Are they pleased with them?

A fascinating fact to share: Ford made 15 million Model T's in under 20 years. The 5,000 accessories available included inflatable dogs and drivers to scare car thieves away.

Lesson 15: Car Options

Most cars aren't plain. Most have some **options**. These are usually built-in extras like radios and sun roofs. You can decide on the options for a new car. But for a used car, you can't. You take what you get. Some options are helpful, and some are fun. But be careful when you shop. All options cost extra. They can also mean extra repairs. So think about what you really need before you buy a car.

Challenge: Safe Extras

Salesperson: You're looking at some fine cars. You must have good taste.

Customer: Taste? I don't want to eat my new car. I want to drive it.

S: Of course. Have you looked at that **loaded** white model over there?

C: Loaded? Like a pizza? With all the extras?

S: Yes. Check out the sun roof. And the automatic transmission. It has **cruise control**, too. You put it in "drive" and set the speed. Then the car almost drives itself.

C: Good thing. I'm usually busy with my **cellular phone**. Does this car have one?

S: No. That's an **accessory** we don't carry. It's an **aftermarket** item. You add it after you get the car.

C: What else does this beauty have?

S: **ABS**—that's an **anti-lock braking system**. It helps avoid skids in bad weather. **Dual** air bags, one on each side. **Leather** seats. And a **theft alarm**. You don't want your phone stolen.

C: Any other safety features?

S: **Daytime running lights.** They're on all the time for better **visibility**.

C: But what about the most important safety feature? What kind of **stereo system** does it have?

S: It's got the very best radio, **cassette**, and **CD** system you can get. You can't find better sound for the price anywhere. But I'm not sure the sound system is a safety feature.

C: Is it loud?

S: Very loud if you turn it up.

C: That's what makes it a safety feature. If I play it loud, people hear me and get out of the way. That's important because I drive very fast. You won't believe how fast I drive.

S: I see.

C: Hey, I like this car. How about a test drive?

Here's your challenge: Should the salesperson let the customer have a test drive? You decide.

44

Life Skills Literacy:
Things to Know About Cars and Driving

Lesson 15: Car Options
Word List

option(s)	accessory	dual	visibility
loaded	aftermarket	leather	stereo system
cruise control	anti-lock braking	theft alarm	cassette
cellular phone	system (ABS)	daytime running lights	CD (compact disc)

Increasing Your Understanding

1. Look at the word list. If you don't know a word, find out what it means. Try to figure it out from the way it is used on page 44. Or look it up in a dictionary.

2. Supply the missing words from the word list:
   (a) Most cars aren't plain, says the top paragraph on page 44. Most cars have some _____.
   (b) The salesperson in the story says the car has _____ for better visibility.
   (c) One of the options in the white car is _____ seats.
   (d) The car doesn't have a cellular phone. The salesperson says that's an _____ item.
   (e) The customer thinks the _____ is the most important safety feature in the car.

Questions to Discuss

1. How did you answer the challenge on page 44? Does the salesperson think the customer may be a bad driver? Why?

2. Can you invent a new car option? What will it be? Brainstorm your ideas with classmates.

3. What do options do? Some options improve car safety. Some do other things. Decide at least three things that different options do. Then list three groups of options that do each thing. Put at least four options in each group. Here's a start: Air bags go in the safety group.

Things to Write About

1. Imagine that the salesperson in the story does not let the customer drive the car. The customer goes away mad. What will the salesperson's boss say? Write a short dialogue.

2. What if the customer does drive the car? What might happen? Write your ideas.

Things to Do

1. Act out the story on page 44 with a partner. Use your own words if you want. Do you think the salesperson is good? Talk about that.

2. Which options are important? Number the list at the top of page 44 from 1 to 7. Put 1 in front of the most important item, 2 in front of the next most important item, and so on.

3. What kind of options make a car look better? Imagine that you and a small group of classmates work for a car maker. You have to think of new options to make cars look good. Come up with at least three ideas.

4. What options do most people like? Ask some people outside the classroom. Then share what you find with classmates. Did they find the same thing?

Life Skills Literacy:
Things to Know About Cars and Driving

Lesson 16: Laws About Cars

TEACHER PAGE

Themes:

- Learning about laws
- Becoming a traffic officer

Background notes: Full knowledge of auto-mobile and traffic laws in the United States and Canada is virtually impossible, because laws vary so much by state and province. Most students will be interested primarily in the laws that apply to them in their own areas. Some of the activities and questions suggested for this topic will help them determine how they can learn more about these laws. If students are interested in more information than you can immediately provide, assign them to research answers and report back to the class.

Preparation possibilities:

- Think about: local issues involving car and traffic laws
- Bring to class: appropriate local news reports; official driver manuals with legal information

Technology resources:

- Search topics: *traffic laws*; state and local enforcement agencies by name
- Web pages to try: Massachusetts Registry of Motor Vehicles

Student pages:

- Page 47 includes: a typical statement of state law about safety inspections (with a readability level of close to 11th grade); a brief discussion of traffic law; a dialogue about joining the highway patrol
- Page 48 includes: a word list you may adjust for your class and student activities

Especially for ESL: Natives of the United States and Canada almost all assimilate some knowledge of car and traffic laws as they grow up. Newcomers may need more help. Ask: How do the laws here compare to those of your first country? How do traffic police here compare to those you have known before?

Extra idioms and slang to introduce:

- *Get off*: escape conviction and punishment
- *Throw the book at somebody*: Punish some-body severely

Thoughts to share with learners: There's a saying that "ignorance of the law is no excuse." That means that each of us must know the law or risk getting into trouble. Reading the laws as lawyers and judges do can be very difficult. But knowing enough about the law to avoid prob-lems is something we can all do.

Questions to ask learners: What are some other words that come to mind when you think about traffic law? What happens in this area when drivers speed? Do they get tickets? A traf-fic summons? What are the penalties like? Do they involve fines? Points? Do you have any experiences with the law you want to share? What if you don't understand a law? Whom can you ask? What should you do if you get stopped by a police officer? What if you get a serious ticket? Or arrested? Who can help you?

Projects to assign learners: Get driver manu-als for your area and review the laws they contain. Bring newspaper reports about traffic courts to class for sharing and discussion.

A fascinating fact to share: The first modern traffic light was installed by the city of Cleve-land, Ohio, in 1914.

Lesson 16: Laws About Cars

All motor vehicles **bearing** a state license plate must have a **current** state inspection before being **operated** on any **public way**. These inspections must be done at an **official inspection station** once a year. Check with any of these stations for details. Failure to have a current inspection sticker could mean a **fine** and loss of **points** on your driver's license. A police officer may **conduct** a vehicle safety inspection at any time.

There are many laws about cars. The **federal government** makes some. Towns and cities make others. But states and provinces make most of them. Some laws are hard to understand. But knowing what they say is important. People who don't may get in trouble. They could break the law or have an accident. The box at the left shows one state law. It talks about safety inspections. They must be done every year in that state.

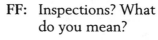

Dialogue: Speeding *Legally?*

First Friend: I love my **motorcycle**. I love riding on it as fast as I can go.

Second Friend: I'm glad there are speed limits. Otherwise, you might break your neck.

FF: I think I'll become a **highway patrol** officer. Then I can ride my motorcycle as fast as the cars I chase. I can even go faster than they do.

SF: I don't think you should be a police officer.

FF: Why not? I am brave enough.

SF: Yes, you are brave enough. But you are also foolish about speeding. And you don't like to study.

FF: Studying is for school. Police don't have to study. They are much too busy chasing speeders.

SF: That's wrong. I have two friends who are **traffic** police. They both studied a whole lot. They didn't spend all their time speeding around on motorcycles.

FF: But what did they study? Didn't they already know what the traffic laws are? I know, and I didn't go to any special school.

SF: They knew some. But there are lots of car laws. There are laws about driving and laws about owning cars. There are laws about insurance and laws about inspections. There are all sorts of laws.

FF: Inspections? What do you mean?

SF: In some states you have to get safety inspections of your car every year. Different states have different laws, you know.

FF: You mean you have to study 50 different sets of laws?

SF: Not in detail. But you have to know a little about what other states do. And there are more laws in Canada.

FF: I don't think I will be a police officer. I think I will be a race car driver instead.

SF: At least you'll be able to speed legally. Good luck!

47

Life Skills Literacy:
Things to Know About Cars and Driving

Lesson 16: Laws About Cars

Word List

ACTIVITY
PAGE

bear(ing)	public way	fine	federal government	highway patrol
current	official inspection	point(s)	legally	traffic
operate(d)	station	conduct	motorcycle	

Increasing Your Understanding

1. Look at the word list. If you don't know a word, find out what it means. Try to figure it out from the way it is used on page 47. Or look it up in a dictionary.

2. Supply the missing words from the word list:

   (a) In the story on page 47, the first friend wants to be a _____ officer.

   (b) The second friend has two other friends who are _____ police.

   (c) The words in the box at the top of the previous page talk about all vehicles _____ a state license plate.

   (d) The law says a police officer may _____ a vehicle safety inspection at any time.

   (e) Failure to have a current sticker could mean a _____ and _____ on your driver's license.

Questions to Discuss

1. Why does the second friend think the first friend should not become a traffic officer? From what the story says, do you agree?

2. Is it okay to have no speed limits? There are no speed limits on some big highways in Montana. Is that a good idea? Would it work in your area?

3. What new traffic or car laws does your state or province need? What laws should it change? Get rid of? Brainstorm your ideas with classmates.

Things to Write About

1. Help stop a speeder. Imagine that the same car speeds past the place where you live every day at 5 P.M. Write a letter to the police telling them about it. Make up a description of the car.

2. What should happen to a driver who speeds almost all the time? Write a paragraph giving your ideas.

Things to Do

1. Act out the story on page 47 with a partner. Use your own words if you want. Are there any jobs where it's okay to drive fast? How many can you think of?

2. What sort of person should join the highway patrol? List at least six things you would look for in such a person.

3. Draw a picture for the story on page 47.

4. Do most drivers in your area obey the laws? Look around and see when you are outside the classroom. Then share your findings with your classmates.

Life Skills Literacy:
Things to Know About Cars and Driving

Lesson 17: Insuring Cars

Themes:

- Assessing automotive insurance needs
- Mandatory liability insurance

Background notes: The price of insurance often comes as a shock to first-time car owners, particularly those in groups at high risk for accidents (young males, for example, or large-city residents). The complexity of insurance often comes as puzzlement. What kinds of insurance do I need? How much? Where should I get it? You can use these pages to help your learners begin considering the basics. And you can use suggested discussion and other activities to help them toward the more detailed answers and information they need to fit their own situations.

Preparation possibilities:

- Think about: the balancing point between too little insurance; how much risk is acceptable?
- Bring to class: information about local transportation systems; an insurance policy

Technology resources:

- Search topics: *automobile insurance* (for providers and comparative policy prices)
- Web pages to try: Insurance Institute for Highway Safety

Student pages:

- Page 50 includes: a simplified proof of insurance card, some basics of insurance, and a story about a couple needing insurance (with echoes of O. Henry's "Gift of the Magi")
- Page 51 includes: a word list you may adjust for your class and student activities

Especially for ESL: Here's another area where specialized vocabulary will offer a special challenge. Go as slowly as you need to help learners understand the most essential facts, such as the idea of mandatory liability insurance. Ask: What can you tell us about car insurance in your first country?

Extra idioms and slang to introduce:

- *Insurance poor:* poor because of spending so much money on insurance
- *Iffy:* uncertain, unsure

Thoughts to share with learners: When you think about insurance you need to think about risk. How much do you risk if you have no insurance? If you have no liability insurance, you might risk having to pay for the damage in a serious accident. You might also risk legal action if the state requires insurance. If you have no collision insurance you risk the value of your car. Should you take that risk? Some people say yes for an old, inexpensive car, but no for a new, more valuable car.

Questions to ask learners: Do you understand deductibles? They are what you have to pay for damages before insurance helps. How much will collision insurance help if you total your car? (Value of car minus premiums and minus deductible.) Do you have car insurance? Are you pleased with it?

Projects to assign learners: Make up a math problem based on collision insurance. (Refer to the explanation just given.) Get some insurance application forms to share. Do some look easier to use than others?

A fascinating fact to share: The first insurance contracts were issued in Babylon around 3000 B.C. to cover goods that might be lost at sea.

Lesson 17: Insuring Cars

A-1 AUTO INSURANCE	**STATE OF** <u>Wyoming</u> **MOTOR VEHICLE** **INSURANCE IDENTIFICATION CARD**

INSURED Hector Cortes
POLICY NUMBER HC 3105650   **EFFECTIVE:** Date: 03 10 99
YR 1993   **MAKE** Ford   **EXPIRATION:** Date: 03 10 00
MODEL Taurus
AGENT Tonia Lee
PHONE (507) 555-1516

THIS POLICY MEETS THE REQUIREMENTS OF STATE LAW.

This card shows proof of insurance. Why buy insurance? Many states say you have to. You need it to get license plates. You need it if you get stopped by a traffic officer. You need it if you have an accident. So don't take chances. Get insurance, and don't drive without it. How do you find it? A good **insurance agent** can save you money. Some policies are expensive. But some are cheaper. You can find a good one. When you do, get it and keep the proof in your car.

Story: A Good Policy

Rico opened a present from his wife, Fran. He held up some papers covered with small writing.

"It's great!" he said. "But it's too much to read right now. Tell me what it says."

"It's a car insurance policy," Fran told him. "Here's the **declarations** page on top. It tells what the policy covers. Now you can drive. You don't have to leave your car sitting in the driveway any longer."

"I met a great agent," she told him. The agent said the state required **liability** insurance. That would pay if you caused an accident. It would cover both **property damage** and **bodily injury**. The **collision clause** would cover costs if you damaged your own car.

"Excellent," said Rico. "What about **uninsured motorist coverage**?"

"Yes," said Fran. "It will pay if an uninsured driver hits you. It has **comprehensive**, too. If somebody steals your car, it pays."

"But how could you afford this?" asked Frank.

"I sold my bicycle," she said.

"Oh no! Why?"

"My end of the year **bonus** from work wasn't enough to cover the insurance **premium**. So I sold the bike. But I don't need it. We can use the car now."

"But there's a problem," said Rico. "Look in the driveway."

Fran looked out the window. The car was gone.

"Where is it, Rico?"

"It was just sitting there. So I sold it."

"Oh, no. Then how can we go to Los Angeles next month?"

"We'll use my present to you. I bought it with some of the car money."

Fran opened the gift and found two airplane tickets to Los Angeles.

She laughed. "At least we'll have our trip," she said.

"Yes," answered Rico. "And when we get back we will buy two used bicycles. Then we'll save for another car."

"And another insurance policy," added Fran.

Life Skills Literacy:
Things to Know About Cars and Driving

Lesson 17: Insuring Cars

Word List

insured	expiration	liability	collision clause	comprehensive
policy	insurance agent	property damage	uninsured motorist	bonus
effective	declarations	bodily injury	coverage	premium

Increasing Your Understanding

1. Look at the word list. If you don't know a word, find out what it means. Try to figure it out from the way it is used on page 50. Or look it up in a dictionary.

2. Supply the missing words from the word list:

   (a) In the story on page 50, Fran shows Frank the _____ page from an insurance policy.

   (b) The policy has a _____ in case Frank damages his own car.

   (c) The agent said the state required _____ insurance.

   (d) Fran's bonus wasn't enough to cover the insurance _____.

   (e) The Proof of Insurance Card has places for the _____ date and the _____ date.

Questions to Discuss

1. When in the story does Frank say "Oh no!"? Why does he say it?

2. Is car insurance fair? Young men pay more than other people. Should they? People in big cities pay more, too. Should everybody pay the same price?

3. Should we get rid of insurance? Should the government pay for accidents? Then people wouldn't need insurance. Do you like that idea? Why or why not?

Things to Write About

1. What don't you know about car insurance? Write four or five questions.

2. Imagine that your nephew has a car. But he doesn't have insurance. He had it long enough to get license plates. Then he gave it up. This is illegal. What do you think? Write him a letter telling him.

Things to Do

1. Act out the story on page 50 with a partner. Use your own words if you want. Use your hands and faces to act. Be really surprised about the presents.

2. What else can you insure? Car insurance is just one kind. List three other kinds. Tell what each one does by writing a sentence about it.

3. What makes a good insurance company? Make up a radio ad for First Rate Auto Insurance. Tell people why they should buy it. Read your ad aloud the way it would sound on the radio.

4. Do people you know like their car insurance? Talk to some people outside class. Ask where they got their policy and if they like it. Share what you find out with your classmates.

Lesson 18: Papers for Cars

TEACHER PAGE

Themes:

- Keeping and protecting important car papers
- Being stopped by a police officer

Background notes: Paperwork. The piles are intimidating to almost everybody. But some of the papers in them are more important than others. These pages will help you build learner understanding of just which car-related papers deserve the most careful treatment. The challenge story and word list focus on just a few highly significant documents. But students will probably surprise themselves with the number of others they are able to brainstorm (see the second item under "Questions to Discuss" on page 54).

Preparation possibilities:

- Think about: paperwork storage procedures that work for you
- Bring to class: some of your own car papers

Technology resources:

- Search topics: *automobiles*, then *police*
- Web pages to try: California Department of Motor Vehicles (forms associated with car operation and ownership)

Student pages:

- Page 53 includes: a simplified car registration, an introduction to the paperwork of cars, and a challenge story involving important car papers
- Page 54 includes: a word list you may adjust for your class and student activities

Especially for ESL: Paperwork can pile up fast for some people new to the United States and Canada. Your learners may benefit from talking to each other about which papers are most important. You might include items like passports and citizenship records in any discussions about paperwork storage.

Extra idioms and slang to introduce:

- *Clam up:* become silent
- *Clunker:* worn-out car

Thoughts to share with learners: Making a copy of every important paper is a good idea. It's good to know something about different police procedures. When police arrest somebody, they usually take that person to the police station, court, or jail. A summons says to appear in court at a later time. Most tickets are summonses. A written warning says to be careful and not do something (like speeding) again.

Questions to ask learners: Do you have good places to store papers? Do you know good places to get them copied? Can you think of any reason not to carry ownership papers in your car? (Think about possible car theft.) What can you do if you think there's a problem? (Make copies and store them elsewhere.)

Projects to assign learners: Visit a bank and ask about safety deposit boxes. How much do they cost? At home, organize your own important papers. Think about copying some.

A fascinating fact to share: Riding a motorcycle at 50 miles an hour in 35-degree weather is the equivalent of standing still at a temperature of −1° Fahrenheit.

Lesson 18: Papers for Cars

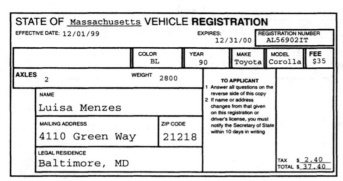

STATE OF <u>Massachusetts</u> VEHICLE **REGISTRATION**

EFFECTIVE DATE: 12/01/99

EXPIRES: 12/31/00   REGISTRATION NUMBER AL56902IT

| | COLOR BL | YEAR 90 | MAKE Toyota | MODEL Corolla | FEE $35 |

AXLES 2   WEIGHT 2800

NAME Luisa Menzes

MAILING ADDRESS 4110 Green Way   ZIP CODE 21218

LEGAL RESIDENCE Baltimore, MD

TO APPLICANT
1 Answer all questions on the reverse side of this copy
2 If name or address changes from that given on this registration or driver's license, you must notify the Secretary of State within 10 days in writing

TAX $ 2.40
TOTAL $ 37.40

Here's a car registration. It gives proof of car ownership. It tells who a car belongs to. Another important car paper is the **bill of sale**. That shows who bought the car. Cars have many important papers, and all should be in a safe place. You can keep some in your car. Others can be in your wallet or a file at home. But remember where everything is. If a police officer stops you, you will need the papers. You will need them again when you sell the car.

Challenge: Where Are Those Papers?

Young Driver: Good evening, officer. Did I do something wrong?

Police Officer: You came through that **construction zone** pretty fast, didn't you?

YD: I didn't think so. I was just keeping up with traffic.

PO: And why didn't you pull over sooner? **Failure** to stop is a **moving violation**. I could arrest you for that.

YD: Arrest? Don't do that! My father would kill me! This is his car, and he'll be mad if I get a **court summons**, too. I don't even want a **warning**.

PO: Nobody does. Maybe you should have pulled over sooner.

YD: I'm sorry. I saw your **flashing lights** and I heard your **siren**. I thought you wanted to get by me, not stop me.

PO: Let's have a look at your license.

YD: It's somewhere in my wallet. Look at all this junk. Here it is!

PO: Now your registration and proof of insurance.

YD: My father keeps those in the **glove compartment**.

PO: Then open it slowly and carefully. I'll shine my light on it. Then put all the stuff on the **passenger** seat.

YD: Okay. Hey, where are those papers?

PO: Suppose you tell me.

YD: I bet I know! I think he just got new license plates. I bet he took the papers out then. Hey, look! What's this?

PO: Looks like gloves to me.

YD: Just like my father. Who else puts gloves in a glove compartment? That's interesting, isn't it?

PO: I tell you what interests me. The report I just got of a stolen car. A blue Toyota just like this.

YD: But this is my father's car! Honest!

PO: Suppose you just step out of that car—very, very slowly.

Here's your challenge: You are the young driver. This really is your father's car. What do you say? What do you do?

Life Skills Literacy:
Things to Know About Cars and Driving

Lesson 18: Papers for Cars

Word List

registration	bill of sale	moving violation	flashing lights	passenger
axle(s)	construction zone	court summons	siren	
fee	failure	warning	glove compartment	

Increasing Your Understanding

1. Look at the word list. If you don't know a word, find out what it means. Try to figure it out from the way it is used on page 53. Or look it up in a dictionary.

2. Supply the missing words from the word list:

   (a) The box at the top of page 53 shows a vehicle _____.

   (b) Another important car paper is the _____, according to the paragraph near the box.

   (c) The police officer in the story says the driver came through a _____ pretty fast.

   (d) Later, the driver has to put things from the glove compartment on the _____ seat.

   (e) The driver saw the officer's _____ and heard a _____.

Questions to Discuss

1. Why does the police officer shine a light on the glove compartment? Why does the officer tell the driver to take things out slowly?

2. What are some other important papers connected with cars? Brainstorm your answers.

3. Should you keep all your important car papers in the glove compartment? What could go wrong if you did?

Things to Write About

1. Imagine that you are the young driver in the story. Write a paragraph saying how you feel.

2. Is speeding ever okay? Imagine that a police officer stops you for driving too fast. Write down three or four reasons you might give for speeding.

Things to Do

1. Act out the story on page 53 with a partner. Use your own words if you want. Can you think of a happy ending for this story? Write down your ideas.

2. Role-play a telephone conversation between the young driver and the young driver's father. The driver is at the police station, under arrest. The father is at home.

3. Make a sign telling drivers to go slow in a construction zone.

4. Does anybody really put their gloves in a glove compartment? Ask around outside class. Ask what people do keep there. Share your answers in class.

Life Skills Literacy:
Things to Know About Cars and Driving

Lesson 19: The Writing on Cars

TEACHER PAGE

Theme:

- Reading the information in and on cars

Background notes: Would people be safer if they read all the labels and messages on their cars more closely? Would they maintain their vehicles better? Nobody knows, of course. But these pages should help you at least prompt learner interest in all the writing carried by cars. You can also use them as the starting point for discussion of topics like parking rules and regulations in your area, car theft, and learning styles. (See "Questions to ask learners," below, the first discussion question on page 57, and a related question in the writing activities of page 21.)

Preparation possibilities:

- Think about: the messages you see inside cars
- Bring to class: a car manual; notes on any car messages you find particularly useful

Technology resources:

- Search topics: *air bags* and similar devices covered in written car notices
- Web pages to try: Allstate Insurance Company (for information from the National Insurance Crime Bureau on Vehicle Identification Numbers)

Student pages:

- Page 56 includes: a safety notice about seat belts; an introduction to and a dialogue about the writing on cars
- Page 57 includes: a word list you may adjust for your class and student activities

Especially for ESL: ESL learners in some areas may be able to help each other locate written materials in their first languages. Ask: Are the messages on cars here like what you found in your first countries? What are the differences?

Extra idioms and slang to introduce:

- *Buckle up:* Fasten your seat belt
- *Buckle down:* get serious about doing something

Thoughts to share with learners: Vehicle identification numbers (VIN's) are important for car registration and in tracing stolen vehicles. Keeping a record of your VIN outside the car is important.

Questions to ask learners: Who in the class owns a car? Do you know your VIN? Do you have it recorded somewhere? Which do you like better: symbols showing you what car controls like wiper switches are? Or words? Do different cars have different notices? Do you think most car owners read everything on their cars? Everything in their car manuals? Should they?

Projects to assign learners: Explore your own car or that of a good friend. Count all the written messages you find in it, and report to the class. Copy some of the symbols you find in cars and share them. Find one written message you didn't know was in your car and share it. Design a vanity plate for yourself.

A fascinating fact to share: The FBI reports that just under 1.5 million motor vehicle thefts were reported in 1995, the lowest number since 1989.

Lesson 19: The Writing on Cars

CAUTION
TO AVOID SERIOUS INJURY
For <u>maximum protection</u> in all types of crashes, always wear your safety bolt. Do not install <u>rearward-facing</u> child seats in any front passenger's seat position.

You need to read a lot to understand your car. Some car manuals have hundreds of pages. And most cars have a lot of labels like the one in the box at the left. Some of the language about cars is **technical** and hard to understand. If you are not sure what some of it means, get help. Ask a friend or a teacher to help you with the reading. Or call your car dealer and ask about the car.

Dialogue: A Good Book

First Friend: Read anything good recently?

Second Friend: Yes. My car.

FF: Get serious. You can't read a car.

SF: Of course you can. There's writing all over it. The best parts are my license plates. Mine are **vanity** plates.

FF: I saw those. They have your name on them.

SF: And there are safety **labels** all over the place. Inside the driver's door. On the back of the sun **visor**. That one talks about seat belts and crashes. That's scary to think about.

FF: You make your car sound like a book.

SF: It's almost as good. Some of it's even in **code**.

FF: Like what?

SF: Like the letters and numbers on the tires. They tell about the tire size and other details. You need to know the code to understand them. Then there's the **Vehicle Identification Number**. Some people call it the "VIN." It's on a metal tag under the windshield.

FF: That's the **serial number** of your car. No other car has the same number. I hope you wrote it down somewhere.

SF: I don't need to. I know it by heart.

FF: You take this reading seriously, don't you?

SF: Too seriously, sometimes. Yesterday it cost me.

FF: How?

SF: I was in a coffee shop reading my car manual. It's 375 pages long, and I forgot about the **parking meter**.

VEHICLE IDENTIFICATION NUMBER

FF: Uh-oh.

SF: Right. The meter **expired** while I was reading. When I got to the car I had a ticket. It said I was in **violation** of the parking code.

FF: How much do they want?

SF: A $25 **waiver fee**. It's like a fine. I pay or go to court.

FF: I would just pay it.

SS: I will. In fact I'm going to the bank now.

FF: Okay. Happy travels. And happy reading.

Life Skills Literacy:
Things to Know About Cars and Driving

Name_____ Date _____

Lesson 19: The Writing on Cars
Word List

ACTIVITY
PAGE

caution	rearward-facing	label(s)	Vehicle Identification Number (VIN)	expire(d)
maximum	technical	visor	serial number	violation
protection	vanity	code	parking meter	waiver fee

Increasing Your Understanding

1. Look at the word list. If you don't know a word, find out what it means. Try to figure it out from the way it is used on page 56. Or look it up in a dictionary.

2. Supply the missing words from the word list:

   (a) The second friend in the story on page 56 has to pay a $25 _____.

   (b) The first friend says the VIN is the _____ of the car.

   (c) The second friend says there are safety _____ all over the place.

   (d) The label at the top of page 56 says what to do for _____ safety protection in crashes.

   (e) You should not install _____ child seats in the front passenger's seat.

Questions to Discuss

1. How does the second friend in the story on page 56 like to learn things? Is that the best way for everybody to learn about cars? What are some other ways? Is experience a good way to learn about car safety? Why or why not?

2. Is it okay to use code on the outside of car tires? How can consumers find out what the code means? Should the government say tire makers have to use plain language?

3. Maybe cars should have this warning on the dashboard: "Don't lock your keys in the car." What do you think? Can you think of other labels cars should have? Brainstorm your ideas.

Things to Write About

1. Write a simple safety label of your own about seat belts. Put it in your own words.

2. Why do cars have Vehicle Identification Numbers? Who uses them? Do the numbers do any good? Write a paragraph giving your ideas.

Things to Do

1. Act out the story on page 56 with a partner. Use your own words if you want. Decide if you think parking meters are a good idea. Should you have more in your area? Fewer?

2. What does the writing on cars do? Some give safety ideas. List at least three things that other messages do.

3. Why should people read their cars? Make a poster for a dealer's wall. It should tell customers why reading new cars is a good idea.

4. Can you find some interesting vanity plates? Look around outside class, then share what you find with classmates.

Lesson 20: Driving for Pay

Theme:

- Driving professionally

Background notes: In 1995, nine million people were employed in jobs related to trucking, according to the American Trucking Association. Among the employers were 380,000 trucking companies. Add to that the limousine, taxi, and bus industries located throughout North America and you have a huge employment opportunity. These pages will help your students explore that opportunity and decide whether it holds appeal for them. As you use the pages, you might point out that reading and writing can both be important for professional drivers. You can also encourage learners to continue developing those skills in ways that can help prepare them for driving jobs (learning the vocabulary of cars and trucks, understanding highway signs, and using maps, for example).

Preparation possibilities:

- Think about: professional driving opportunities in your area
- Bring to class: information about commercial licenses and training courses

Technology resources:

- Search topics: *trucking, truck driver schools* and other specialty areas
- Web pages to try: American Trucking Association, Greyhound Bus Lines (lists employment opportunities)

Student pages:

- Page 59 includes: an introduction to professional driving and a story about a problem at a professional truck driving school

- Page 60 includes: a word list you may adjust for your class and student activities

Especially for ESL: Note: People just learning English often become cab drivers in some American cities. Ask: Is this true in your area? How do such drivers succeed while still learning English? Is professional driving here the same as in your first country?

Extra idioms and slang to introduce:

- *Rig:* large truck or bus
- *Keep on trucking:* keep doing an activity (like working)

Thoughts to share with learners: Page 60 (the second item under "Questions to Discuss") talks about professional drivers and the senses of sight, sound, touch, taste, and smell. But drivers also need another kind of sense—common sense. That may be most important of all.

Questions to ask learners: Who in the class drives for money? Do you like the job? Who would like to drive for pay? How do you plan to get started?

Projects to assign learners: In small groups, plan a truck trip from San Francisco, California to Seatle, Washington. Use a map and decide what roads to take. How many days will you need? Where will you stop to sleep? Talk to some professional drivers. Do they like their jobs? Share your answers with classmates. Find out about commercial licenses in your area. How do you get them? Are there schools you can go to?

A fascinating fact to share: Women represented about 5 percent of American truck drivers in 1993.

Lesson 20: Driving for Pay

Driving for pay can be great. Truckers travel to many areas and see a lot. **Emergency** drivers help other people. **Cab** drivers meet many people, and race drivers get excitement. The pay can be good, and the days aren't all the same. But some people get nervous in traffic. Others like offices, and some don't want to travel. These people shouldn't have driving jobs. What about you? Do you want to drive for pay? Does the school in this ad sound good?

Story: Which Way to Turn?

Myrna wanted to be a **professional** driver. She hoped to see all of North America from a truck. So she **enrolled** in a truck drivers' school.

She was a good student. She read every **assignment** carefully. She learned how to get a **commercial** license.

The first time Myrna climbed into the cab of a **tractor-trailer** she was thrilled. She drove slowly forward around the training course. "Good job," her teacher said.

The next week, Myrna had to **put** the truck **in reverse** and back up. That's when the trouble started. Myrna was used to backing her car. If she turned the wheel right, the car backed to the right. If she turned left, it went left.

Backing trailers is different. When you turn the wheel right, the trailer goes left. When you turn the wheel left, the trailer goes right. That sounds simple, but it isn't. In a **semi**, you can't even turn around to see where you are going. You have to use the outside mirrors. Doing that confused Myrna.

"It's going the wrong way!" she shouted at her teacher.

"You're turning the wrong way!" he shouted back.

Myrna was watching the training school in the mirror. It was getting very close.

"Stop!" yelled the instructor.

But the truck hit the building. In the mirror, Myrna saw **bricks** falling. When she jumped out to check the damage, she hurt her ankle badly. She landed in bed for two days.

Myrna's friend Yong went to visit her.

"My teacher said I can try again," said Myrna. "But I'm not sure I want to."

"What will you do instead?" asked Yong.

"I may be an **inventor**."

"Really?" Yong said. "But it's hard to think of brand-new ideas."

"I already know my first **invention**," Myrna told him. "A **foam rubber** trailer for student truck drivers."

Life Skills Literacy:
Things to Know About Cars and Driving

Name_____ Date _____

Lesson 20: Driving for Pay

Word List

ACTIVITY PAGE

accredit(ed)	professional	commercial	semi	foam rubber
emergency	enroll(ed)	tractor-trailer	brick(s)	
cab	assignment	put (something) in reverse	inventor/invention	

Increasing Your Understanding

1. Look at the word list. If you don't know a word, find out what it means. Try to figure it out from the way it is used on page 59. Or look it up in a dictionary.

2. Supply the missing words from the word list:

   (a) The ad at the top of page 59 says the school is fully _____.

   (b) The paragraph beside the ad says that _____ drivers help other people.

   (c) At the end of the story, Myrna says she might be an _____.

   (d) The trouble began when Myrna _____ the truck _____.

   (e) Myrna read every assignment and learned how to get a _____ license.

Questions to Discuss

1. If you became a truck driver, what kind of truck would you drive? Large? Small? Long-distance? Local? What are the best things about long-distance trucking? The worst things?

2. What senses are most important for professional drivers? Sight? Hearing? Taste? Touch? Smell? Which ones are important? Which ones are not? Give your reasons.

3. How many kinds of professional drivers can you think of? Brainstorm your answers.

Things to Write About

1. Imagine that you are applying for truck driver training school. Write a letter saying why you want to enroll.

2. What kind of people make good ambulance drivers? Write a paragraph giving some of your ideas.

Things to Do

1. With a partner, role-play the parts of Myrna and Yong in the story on page 59. Yong should tell Myrna to go back to the school. What will happen if she does? You decide.

2. What do truck drivers need? Imagine that you are taking a 10-day truck trip. Make a list of at least eight things you will take with you.

3. Make up a radio ad for a truck driving school. Tell people why driving trucks is a good job. Read the ad aloud the way you would read it on the radio. Use sound effects if you want.

4. Who wants to go where? Ask some people outside class to imagine they drive long-distance trucks. Where do they want to go? Share your answers with classmates.

Life Skills Literacy:
Things to Know About Cars and Driving

Lesson 21: Road Signs

TEACHER PAGE

Themes:
- Understanding road signs
- Thinking about highway safety

Background notes: Official traffic signs emerged over the twentieth century as a unique and effective international language. They are now controlled in the United States by the Federal Highway Administration through its *Manual on Uniform Traffic Control Devices.* Non-government signs have flourished with fewer controls, although various environmental and health movements have made some changes in recent years. Some states, like Maine, have banned billboards almost entirely. But despite their different origins and controls, both types of signs must be considered when traffic safety is discussed, and both are mentioned in these pages.

Preparation possibilities:
- Think about: any signage problems and issues in your area
- Bring to class: illustrations of signs, available in some driver manuals

Technology resources:
- Search topics: *traffic signs*
- Web pages to try: Federal Highway Administration, Government Printing Office (offers the traffic manual mentioned above under "Background notes")

Student pages:
- Page 62 includes: an introduction to the topic of official signs and a challenge story about signs and safety

- Page 63 includes: a word list you may adjust for your class and student activities

Especially for ESL: Are signs the same around the world? Ask: What were official signs like in your native country? What about non-government signs?

Extra idioms and slang to introduce:
- *In the driver's seat:* in control
- *Tailgate:* follow another vehicle too closely

Thoughts to share with learners: Pranks involving traffic signs have sometimes led to serious injury and death. The first activity under "Things to Do" on page 63 is therefore important. Federal, state, provincial, and local governments are all involved in placing signs. Who does what depends on whether a road is federal, state or provincial, or local. Long, straight roads can be dangerous, too, because people sometimes get bored and sleepy when driving on them.

Questions to ask learners: Who in the class has ever been confused by official road signs? Where was this? What happened? Do you know of any areas where signs have ruined nice views of scenery?

Projects to assign learners: Find a place near you where signs are a problem for some reason. Do something about it—like writing a letter to your town or city government.

A fascinating fact to share: Traffic signs used to be different in different parts of the United States. The first manual to help make them standard appeared in 1935.

Lesson 21: Road Signs

Traffic signs "speak" three ways. One way is color. Stop signs are red, and curve signs are yellow. Signs showing places are often green. A second way signs speak is shape. Stop signs have six sides, and **yield** signs have three. Many other signs have four sides. Signs also speak with words and **symbols**. Stop signs use the word "STOP." Curve signs use **arrows**. Many signs are easy to understand, but they can't do all the work. Drivers still need to think about them and use common sense.

Challenge: How Can We Save Lives?

The highway safety record in your state is not good. There are many accidents and **fatalities** each year. You want to improve it. So you join the Safe Highways **Council**. It works on accident **prevention**.

Some members say there are too many road signs. They think that **billboards distract** drivers. The drivers end up looking at the ads, not the road. They don't pay attention to official signs. Official signs are small. But they are important, too. They say things like "Stop" and "Caution." Or they give **information** on road **conditions**. If you don't read them you could be injured, or worse, the members say. So that's why billboards can be dangerous. U.S. **interstate** highways don't have them. State roads shouldn't have them either.

Last year some members tried to get a new law passed. They wanted to **ban** billboards. They thought this would make roads safer. The law also would make the scenery along roads more beautiful, they said. Big signs are ugly. Without them, travelers could see the state better.

But the state **legislature** said no. **Lawmakers** said that people have the right to

advertise. The new law would **interfere** with that right. The law did not pass.

Now the Council is meeting again. Some people on it are angry. "We were right about the law," they say. "But we have failed. Now more people will die." But others say, "It's okay. We'll try for the law again. Soon there will be more accidents. Then the law will pass."

Another member has a new idea. She says the Council should rent its own billboards. This is what she thinks those signs should say:

> SAFETY FIRST!
> STOP READING THIS SIGN!
> WATCH WHERE YOU'RE GOING INSTEAD!

But another member says the new idea is silly.

Here's your challenge: What do you think? What would you do? Do you have a better idea?

Life Skills Literacy:
Things to Know About Cars and Driving

Name_____ Date _____

Lesson 21: Road Signs

Word List

ACTIVITY PAGE

yield	fatalities	distract	interstate	legislature
symbol(s)	council	information	ban	lawmaker(s)
arrow(s)	prevention	condition(s)	billboard(s)	interfere

Increasing Your Understanding

1. Look at the word list. If you don't know a word, find out what it means. Try to figure it out from the way it is used on page 62. Or look it up in a dictionary.

2. Supply the missing words from the word list:

   (a) The story on page 62 says that some official signs give information about road

   _____.

   (b) Members of the Safe Highways Council work on accident _____.

   (c) The _____ in the legislature said that people have the right to advertise.

   (d) There are many accidents and _____ every year, according to the story.

   (e) The top of page 62 says signs speak three ways. The third way is by words and

   _____.

Questions to Discuss

1. Why do the people in the story want to ban billboards? What else can they do to prevent accidents?
2. Should all official road signs have words on them? Just symbols like arrows? Which work best?
3. How many official road signs can you think of? Brainstorm this in class. Show what the signs look like if you can. Draw them on a chalkboard or poster paper.

Things to Write About

1. What do you think about billboards? Should they be banned? Write a paragraph giving your answer.
2. Imagine that somebody had changed a speed limit sign near where you live. It used to say 35 miles an hour. Now it says 85.

Write a letter to your town or city streets department. Say why the sign needs to be fixed soon.

Things to Do

1. What should happen to people who take down STOP signs for a joke? Role-play a meeting of a Safe Highways Council with several classmates. What do you think the law should say?
2. What road signs are near you? Make a list of five road signs near your home or school. Say where each one is and what it does.
3. Draw symbols for these three signs: school crossing, hospital zone, do not enter.
4. Does a place near you need better signs? Fewer signs? Look around outside class. Then share your ideas with your classmates.

Life Skills Literacy:
Things to Know About Cars and Driving

Lesson 22: Accidents

Themes:

- What to do when accidents happen
- Preventing accidents

Background notes: The seriousness of accidents can be determined in part by how victims, witnesses, and others respond to them. Unfortunately, accidents don't bring out the best in everybody. Some people panic, while others try to profit. Some people react with common sense and speed. They do just what must be done, and sometimes more, to make a bad situation better. These pages will help you equip your learners with the understanding and preparation they need to join this second group. Topical questions and activities will also help prompt discussion of accident prevention.

Preparation possibilities:

- Think about: police and other emergency services available in your area; accident reporting procedures (the well-known 911 is not yet universal)
- Bring to class: accident forms from local police or insurance agencies

Technology resources:

- Search topics: *emergency services*
- Web pages to try: Emergency Services Network (and links)

Student pages:

- Page 65 includes: part of an accident report form; basic thoughts about responding to accidents; a dialogue between an accident victim and an insurance company representative
- Page 66 includes: a word list you may adjust for your class and student activities

Especially for ESL: Learners new to English-speaking environments may in moments of excitement revert to their first languages. Talk with students about this possibility. Ask them to role-play some calls and conversations based on emergency situations.

Extra idioms and slang to introduce:

- *Hit the panic button:* panic
- *Hit-and-run:* an accident in which a driver leaves the scene without stopping

Thoughts to share with learners: People in accidents need to be careful about what they say. They should not talk about how much insurance they have. They should not say, "It's my fault." They should wait until they are calm and can remember exactly what happened.

Questions to ask learners: Does anything good ever come out of accidents? Does anybody have a story about that to share? How do you know if you need a lawyer after an accident? How can you find a good one?

Projects to assign learners: Do you have to report every tiny little accident? Find out what accidents must be reported. (In some states, property damage at a certain level or personal injury makes an accident reportable.) Bring newspaper reports of local accidents to class. Tell classmates how the accidents might have been avoided.

A fascinating fact to share: In 1969, a man's car broke down near Moscow. He had it towed all the way to West Berlin. The distance was 1,456 miles. That was a record, according to the *Guinness Book of World Records.*

Lesson 22: Accidents

INJURIES AND/OR FATALITIES CAUSED BY THE ACCIDENT					
NAME AND ADDRESS	☐ Injury ☐ Fatal	☐ Under Age 18	☐ Driver ☐ Passenger	☐ In Your Vehicle ☐ In Other Vehicle	☐ Bycyclist ☐ Pedestrian
NAME AND ADDRESS	☐ Injury ☐ Fatal	☐ Under Age 18	☐ Driver ☐ Passenger	☐ In Your Vehicle ☐ In Other Vehicle	☐ Bycyclist ☐ Pedestrian
DAMAGE TO OTHER PROPERTY (Telephone poles, fences, etc.)					
PROPERTY OWNER'S NAME AND ADDRESS			DAMAGES OVER $500? ☐ YES ☐ NO		
I CERTIFY under PENALTY of PERJURY that this information is true and correct.					
DATE	SIGN HERE X				

Accidents can be bad, and nobody wants one. But if you do have one, don't **panic**. That can make things worse. Be **calm**, but act fast. Call the police, and ask for an ambulance if you need it. Then help anybody who is injured. Get the names of people at the accident. Don't forget to call your insurance company. Probably it will want a written report. So will the police. Here's part of a form used by one police department.

Dialogue: What Happened?

Policy Holder: My car is insured through your company and I need to report an accident.

Insurance Representative: I'm sorry to hear that. What's your policy number?

PH: It's 00304189.

IR: Did this accident cause any injury or **death**?

PH: The other driver had a cut finger. Nobody else was hurt.

IR: Good. It's bad enough to have a damaged car. Now, tell me what happened.

PH: I was driving East on Main Street in Canton. At Pinewood Avenue, I had a green light and went ahead. But another car came straight at me and slammed into the right side of my car.

IR: Do you know why it happened?

PH: The other driver had a **vision** problem. He said the sun **reflected** off his car and **blinded** him. I'm worried he'll think it was my fault.

IR: Don't worry. If your report is **accurate**, this accident wasn't anybody's fault. Now, can you still drive your car?

PH: No. I can't turn the steering wheel. I had to get a tow. The car is at Fixer's Garage.

IR: They can estimate the damage. If it seems okay to us, you can go ahead with repairs. Now some other details. Did you call the police?

PH: Yes. I had some real damage. I knew this was a **reportable** accident. Calling 911 for the police was almost the first thing we did. A **patrol car** came right away.

IR: Were there **witnesses**?

PH: Yes. I got their names at the scene.

IR: That's good. But what was the very first thing you did after the accident?

PH: I jumped out of my car and yelled at the other driver.

IR: That's not so good.

PH: I know. But it sure made me feel better! Until he said he was a **lawyer**.

Life Skills Literacy:
Things to Know About Cars and Driving

Lesson 22: Accidents

Word List

certify	panic	death	blind(ed)	reportable
penalty	calm	vision	lawyer	patrol car
perjury	representative	reflect(ed)	accurate	witness

Increasing Your Understanding

1. Look at the word list. If you don't know a word, find out what it means. Try to figure it out from the way it is used on page 65. Or look it up in a dictionary.

2. Supply the missing words from the word list:

   (a) In the story on page 65, one driver had a _____ problem.

   (b) The drivers called 911. A _____ came right away.

   (c) The policy holder is nervous because the other driver is a _____.

   (d) The insurance representative asks: "Did this accident cause any injury or _____?"

   (e) The paragraph at the top of page 65 says to be _____ but act fast.

Questions to Discuss

1. Are the drivers in the story calm? Do they have a friendly talk right after the accident? Why might the policy holder be worried when he found out the other driver was a lawyer?

2. What can you do about panic? What if you get too upset or excited after an accident? What do you do?

3. Imagine that you have an accident. It is not your fault. Three people see it. But they won't give their names as witnesses. What should you do?

Things to Write About

1. What causes accidents? Write a paragraph about one major cause. What can be done about it?

2. Imagine that you saw the accident in the story. What did you see? Write a report for the police.

Things to Do

1. Act out the story on page 65 with a partner. But make the accident worse. What happened?

2. Meet with some classmates. Plan some TV ads to cut down on accidents. What will they say? What will they show?

3. Draw a diagram. Show how the accident in the story happened.

4. How many drivers have accidents? Talk to some people outside class. How many have been in car accidents? Seen them? Share what you find with your class.

Life Skills Literacy:
Things to Know About Cars and Driving

Lesson 23: Maps

Theme:

- Using road maps

Background notes: Maps are useful not just for travel but also as teaching tools. They use different learning styles and involve a range of subject areas from math to social studies, so they provide teachers a useful key to understanding student capabilities. And they give learners a chance to use their capabilities in new directions. These pages provide a starting point for considering maps. You might wish to supplement them by having students bring in and share maps that they find useful.

Preparation possibilities:

- Think about: local maps and highway geography (Are streets and avenues laid out in a pattern?)
- Bring to class: maps to share with learners

Technology resources:

- Search topics: *maps*
- Web pages to try: DeLorme, Rand McNally (mapping companies)
- Software to consider: *TripMaker* by Rand McNally; *Map'n' Go* by DeLorme; similar programs

Student pages:

- Page 68 includes: a sample map; an introduction to maps; a story about using maps
- Page 69 includes: a word list you may adjust for your class and student activities

Especially for ESL: Students new to the United States and Canada may find that maps used in connection with these pages help them get their geographical bearings. Ask: Did you use maps a lot in your home country? How? What kind of maps?

Extra idioms and slang to introduce:

- *As the crow flies*: straight distance between two places
- *Off the beaten track:* where not many people go

Thoughts to share with learners: Technology is making great changes in mapping practices. Software programs and the Internet can be used to plan trips. Some cars already have equipment to track their location by computer. Such devices may become increasingly common.

Questions to ask learners: Who in the class uses maps? In connection with cars? For other purposes (like using subways or buses)? Where do you get your road maps? Does anybody belong to the American Automobile Association? Do you use its trip-planning services? How does that work? Have you studied maps in other classes? What have you covered?

Projects to assign learners: Bring a variety of maps to share with classmates. Visit a local tourist office and see what maps are available. Think again about the second item under "Questions to Discuss" on page 69. It asks where you might be starting if you drive two days west and get to Chicago (the Boston area is a possibility). Using a map and working in groups, make up similar problems for your classmates to solve.

A fascinating fact to share: As of 1991, the largest map in the world was a 43-ton relief map of California.

Lesson 23: Maps

There's a trick to using maps, and that's to start with the right one. Maps like this show a lot of area and big highways. But they don't show small roads and other details. Maps with lots of details don't show much area. Which do you need? That depends on where you are going. If your **destination** is a big city, you may need two maps. One can get you there on major highways. The other can help you on small roads when you arrive. You can buy paper maps of all kinds. You can also use computer **programs** to help plan your trip.

Story: Where Did You Go?

You have returned from a vacation. Your friend Asha asks about your travels.

"Where did you go?" she wants to know. "What did you do and what did you see?"

You laugh. You can tell her exactly where you went and what you did with your friends. But you can't tell her much about the **country-side**.

"We drove west for two days," you say. "We stayed with friends in Chicago for a week and had a ball. Then we came back a different way."

"Was the trip beautiful?"

You laugh again. "I saw mostly maps."

"Just maps? No **scenery**?"

"Not much. Frank is a nervous driver. He's always afraid of getting lost. He needs to know where he is every minute. How far have we come? How far to our **motel**? What's the **route number** of this highway? When will we cross the state line? What **direction** are we heading? I think I'll get him a **compass** so he can tell if he's going north or south. I had my eyes on a map most of the way from **departure** to destination."

Asha makes a face. "I hate maps. I never understand them. Fortunately, I have a good sense of direction. I don't need maps very often."

"Frank does. But that's not all. He asks directions at every **tollbooth** and every **service area**. Cars line up behind us while we get **instructions**."

"Better you than me," says Asha.

"I didn't mind," you tell her. "I like math. I like checking the **odometer** to see how far we have come and how far the next **inter-change** is. I like maps, and I learned a lot about them. But there's one thing I still can't figure out."

"What's that?"

"How to fold maps. I think I need a special course in folding maps."

Life Skills Literacy:
Things to Know About Cars and Driving

Name_____ Date _____

Lesson 23: Maps

Word List

destination	scenery	direction	tollbooth	odometer
program(s)	motel	compass	service area	interchange
countryside	route number	departure	instructions	

Increasing Your Understanding

1. Look at the word list. If you don't know a word, find out what it means. Try to figure it out from the way it is used on page 68. Or look it up in a dictionary.

2. Supply the missing words from the word list:

   (a) You laugh in the story on page 68, then say you can't tell Asha much about the _____.

   (b) If Frank gets a _____, he can tell if he's going north or south.

   (c) He asks directions at every _____ and every _____.

   (d) The top of page 68 says you can use maps or computer _____ to plan your trip.

   (e) What map do you need? The paragraph says that depends on your _____.

Questions to Discuss

1. Imagine that you are with Frank in the story on page 68. Do you enjoy the trip? Why or why not? Do you like maps? The math of maps?

2. Where did they come from? The people in the story drove west for two days and got to Chicago. Where do you think they started from? Use a map and math to get your answer.

3. Which roads are better? Imagine driving from New York to Los Angeles. What roads are best? Interstate highways? Smaller ones? Brainstorm reasons for choosing either kind.

Things to Write About

1. Do you have a good sense of direction? Write your answer in a paragraph. Give reasons to support your opinion (maybe you get lost a lot).

2. Write instructions for going from your home to your school. Include a small map if you want.

Things to Do

1. With a partner, act out the parts of the friends in the story on page 68. Use your own names if you want. Do you like using maps? Give your own answers.

2. Should your community have free maps? Imagine that you and some classmates are in your town or city government. Should you spend $5,000 buying maps of the area to give away? List three or four reasons why this is a good idea.

3. Make a map of a car trip you took. It can be a big or little trip. If it's a small one, the map should have more detail.

4. Where can you get maps of your area? Look around the community to see who sells maps. Does anybody offer free maps? Share your information in class.

Life Skills Literacy:
Things to Know About Cars and Driving

Lesson 24: Defensive Driving

TEACHER PAGE

Themes:

- Defensive driving
- Drinking and driving

Background notes: Defensive driving is a wonderful concept that often seems to get more lip service than practice. These pages present the topic for learner consideration and also suggest some of the reasons for it: bad driving in general and drunken driving in particular. Such problems are severe. During 1996 in the United States alone, 17,126 people died in alcohol-related accidents. Use your discussions to help learners see that defensive driving is useful for all of us, not just as punishment administered by the courts.

Preparation possibilities:

- Think about: local defensive driving courses and schools
- Bring to class: newspaper reports about court sentences that include driver training

Technology resources:

- Search topics: *defensive driving*
- Web pages to try: National Safety Council, Mothers Against Drunk Driving (MADD)

Student pages:

- Page 71 includes: part of the warning label from a bottle of an alcoholic beverage; an introduction to reasons for driving defensively; a challenge story about offensive driving
- Page 72 includes: a word list you may adjust for your class and student activities

Especially for ESL: Attitudes of ESL students toward alcohol and aggressive driving can vary greatly according to the customs and attitudes of their home cultures. Be sensitive to such diversity throughout your presentation of these pages. Ask: Does your native country have defensive driving schools or something like them?

Extra idioms and slang to introduce:

- *Have a close call:* just miss a problem or accident
- *Have a fit:* get angry

Thoughts to share with learners: "Designated drivers" don't drink when they take their friends to a place where alcohol is served. This helps them drive defensively and safely. "DWI" or "driving while intoxicated" is a phrase used in many areas. "OUI" or "operating under the influence" is common in other places.

Questions to ask learners: Do you know defensive drivers? Are some people naturally more aggressive drivers than others? What should be done about "habitual offenders"? These are people who break driving laws repeatedly. Can they learn to drive defensively?

Projects to assign learners: Look for information about local defensive driving courses. Try the Yellow Pages of the phone book. Share what you find with the class. Role-play a story about people trying to get one of their friends not to drive while drinking.

A fascinating fact to share: According to the National Safety Council, every weekday night from 10 P.M. to 1 A.M., 1 in 13 drivers is drunk.

Lesson 24: Defensive Driving

CONSUMPTION OF ALCOHOLIC BEVERAGES IMPAIRS YOUR ABILITY TO DRIVE A CAR OR OPERATE MACHINERY, AND MAY CAUSE HEALTH PROBLEMS.

Alcohol and driving don't mix. We have all heard that often. Still, a lot of people drink and drive. They make the roads unsafe. So do many other drivers. Some drive when they are angry about something. Others try to drive and talk on the phone at bad times. And some like to drive too fast. What should the rest of us do? We need to be careful. We need to know that other drivers may cause accidents. We need to drive **defensively**.

Challenge: Who's at Fault?

Boss: Okay, let's hear it. What happened?

Driver: I thought the state trooper told you.

B: I want to hear your **version**. You were driving the company truck on the interstate, right?

D: Yes. Doing fine until I looked in the rear-view mirror and saw a guy in a big sedan **weaving** around behind me. I knew that was trouble.

B: Then he switched lanes?

D: He tried to pass me. But I wouldn't let him. I got right in front of him and slowed down.

B: In my truck?

D: In the company truck, yes. I'm afraid it got a little banged up. That happened when I forced him off the road.

B: I can't believe you did that!

D: He was driving to **endanger**!

B: I want defensive drivers. You were driving **offensively**.

D: I thought he might kill somebody. He had a **suspended** license, too.

B: You didn't know that at the time. And who

put you in charge of **justice**? That's up to the police and the courts.

D: They weren't there. I might have saved a life.

B: You didn't do the truck any good.

D: You should have seen that guy driving!

B: The trooper did say he was under the **influence** and impaired.

D: You could say that. I say he was drunk.

B: Maybe so. But you were **reckless** and **aggressive**. I can't have that.

D: So what happens next? Do I still have a job?

B: You can keep your job on two conditions. First, you take a defensive driving course at your own expense. Second, you pay to repair the truck.

D: But that's $500! That's not fair!

B: Take it or leave it.

Here's your challenge: You are the driver. What do you do? Take it or leave it?

71

Life Skills Literacy:
Things to Know About Cars and Driving

Lesson 24: Defensive Driving

Word List

ACTIVITY PAGE

consumption	defensively	endanger	justice	aggressive
alcoholic beverage(s)	version	offensively	influence	
impair(s)	weaving	suspend(ed)	reckless	

Increasing Your Understanding

1. Look at the word list. If you don't know a word, find out what it means. Try to figure it out from the way it is used on page 71. Or look it up in a dictionary.

2. Supply the missing words from the word list:

   (a) The boss in the story on page 71 asks who put the driver in charge of _____.

   (b) The boss wants to hear the driver's _____ of what happened.

   (c) The driver says the man in the sedan was driving to _____.

   (d) "But you were _____ and _____," says the boss. "I can't have that."

   (e) The label on page 71 says consumption of _____ impairs your ability to drive.

Questions to Discuss

1. How did you answer the challenge on page 71? Do you think the boss was fair? Did the driver act sensibly?

2. What are defensive drivers? How do they drive? Brainstorm your ideas.

3. What should happen to aggressive drivers? Some judges make them go to defensive driving courses. Is that enough? Or should they lose their licenses for a while?

Things to Write About

1. Write a new label to replace the one on page 71. Make yours simpler.

2. Write a newspaper ad for Don's Defensive Driving School. It should say why defensive driving is a good idea.

Things to Do

1. Act out the story on page 71 with a partner. Use your own words if you want. Decide what you think will happen to the driver of the sedan.

2. Make a list of seven things that can be dangerous to have in a car. Alcohol can be one.

3. Draw a picture for the story on page 71.

4. Who knows what defensive driving is? Ask some people you know outside of class about defensive driving. Do they like the idea? Then share what you find with classmates.

Life Skills Literacy:
Things to Know About Cars and Driving

Answers

Words for Completing Sentences:

Page 3: (a) transportation; (b) cheap; (c) parking; (d) insurance; (e) driver's training

Page 6: (a) application; (b) pedestrian; (c) vehicle; (d) parallel; (e) police station

Page 9: (a) trade in; (b) high pressure; (c) practical; (d) demonstrator; (e) make

Page 12: (a) mechanics; (b) manuals; (c) hood; (d) dipstick; (e) wires

Page 15: (a) automated; (b) waxing; (c) supporting; (d) durability; (e) tailpipe

Page 18: (a) steering wheel; (b) rearview mirror; (c) accelerator; (d) speedometer; (e) safety features

Page 21: (a) loan; (b) tax return; (c) borrow; (d) interest; (e) down payment

Page 24: (a) comparison shopping; (b) maintenance agreement; (c) warranty; (d) negotiating; (e) investigate

Page 27: (a) guarantees; (b) Internet; (c) consumer; (d) advice; (e) authorities

Page 30: (a) recommendations; (b) filter; (c) driveway; (d) specialty; (e) reputations

Page 33: (a) pre-owned; (b) slam; (c) fingerprints; (d) lemon; (e) mileage

Page 36: (a) miles per gallon; (b) radiator; (c) discount; (d) regular; (e) quick lube centers

Page 39: (a) deductible; (b) ambulance, tow truck; (c) major; (d) body shops; (e) authorize

Page 42: (a) qualifications; (b) inventory; (c) memory; (d) install; (e) salvage

Page 45: (a) options; (b) daytime running lights; (c) leather; (d) aftermarket; (e) stereo system

Page 48: (a) highway patrol; (b) traffic; (c) bearing; (d) conduct; (e) fine, points

Page 51: (a) declarations; (b) collision clause; (c) liability; (d) premium; (e) effective, expiration

Page 54: (a) registration; (b) bill of sale; (c) construction zone; (d) passenger; (e) flashing lights, siren

Page 57: (a) waiver fee; (b) serial number; (c) labels; (d) maximum; (e) rearward-facing

Page 60: (a) accredited; (b) emergency; (c) inventor; (d) put, in reverse; (e) commercial

Page 63: (a) conditions; (b) prevention; (c) lawmakers; (d) fatalities; (e) symbols

Page 66: (a) vision; (b) patrol car; (c) lawyer; (d) death; (e) calm

Page 69: (a) countryside; (b) compass; (c) tollbooth, service area; (d) programs; (e) destination

Page 72: (a) justice; (b) version; (c) endanger; (d) reckless, aggressive; (e) alcoholic beverages

Share Your Bright Ideas with Us!

We want to hear from you! Your valuable comments and suggestions will help us meet your current and future classroom needs.

Your name_____Date_____

School name_____Phone_____

School address_____

Grade level taught_____Subject area(s) taught_____Average class size_____

Where did you purchase this publication?_____

Was your salesperson knowledgeable about this product?   Yes_____   No_____

What monies were used to purchase this product?

____School supplemental budget   ____Federal/state funding   ____Personal

Please "grade" this Walch publication according to the following criteria:

	A	B	C	D	F
Quality of service you received when purchasing	A	B	C	D	F
Ease of use	A	B	C	D	F
Quality of content	A	B	C	D	F
Page layout	A	B	C	D	F
Organization of material	A	B	C	D	F
Suitability for grade level	A	B	C	D	F
Instructional value	A	B	C	D	F

COMMENTS:_____

_____

What specific supplemental materials would help you meet your current—or future—instructional needs?

_____

Have you used other Walch publications? If so, which ones?_____

May we use your comments in upcoming communications?   ____Yes   ____No

Please **FAX** this completed form to **207-772-3105**, or mail it to:

Product Development, J. Weston Walch, Publisher, P.O. Box 658, Portland, ME 04104-0658

We will send you a **FREE GIFT** as our way of thanking you for your feedback. **THANK YOU!**